Soldier On

Sue White

ISBN No. 978-1-905546-34-3

Soldier On is a story based on fact, only names
have been changed to protect the innocent

This edition published 2007
by Write Books, Ferrybridge
www.writebooks.co.uk

Contents

With Thanks

I just sat thinking about giving thanks to the people who have helped me, for helping us. I realised that if I mentioned everyone that has been important to me or us I could probably fill another book; I have had so many lovely people in my life I am lucky.

My true best friend, and pain in the rear; the man I married twenty years ago this December. Not forgetting the other member in our inner sanctum "the kid".
Every minute of every day I am thankful to them, and for them.

For my family.

We didn't get to choose each other but we chose to stick together. We have all been through some crap or other but we always survive. I love every single one of you in "my family".
Without you I would not, and could not, have survived the last years and I wouldn't be so balanced in myself. We all give and take different things from each other it works well we are a happy group of about fifty five and that includes the dog babies Holly, Rocky and Monty.

We stick together and that's important.

Tina must be mentioned as she read the early pages and encouraged me; she shared my belief.

Simon and Kerry have to be mentioned; they have suffered eye fatigue, blindness and stress in helping me get this book completed.

Friends

Over the years we have made many friends and some of them have picked me up at some stage or another, but I'll group you together so you can identify yourselves; but I can't remember everyone so don't be offended.

From the Army years there were so many. We had a lot of good times in between tours and some of you may recognise us; feel free to get in touch, there will be a website…

The two most important are in the book, and I love them and thank them for their love and support from the start; our best friends at the start and still on call today; thanks to you both.

Friends of our whole family; Twinarooni, Liz, Sue, Pat, Carol and all the others from a very small place, famous for its own elite sausages close to Harrogate, Kirsty, I am so glad your thirty.

The guys from the telecoms company who tried to understand; there were four or five; best not name them they might sue me!

Some people I have met through work have helped in only ways they will need to know, Hilary, Peter, Janis, Andy and Claire and the others…I would describe it as my first really rewarding, happy job. I moaned about it at the time but it taught me a lot about many things; the work and the people, both staff and clients

My tutor and fellow "adult learners" at college; Maureen who picked up on my interest in Mental Health and kept me in college is now teaching my son. I am thankful she got me interested in learning about "mental health what makes us tick".

What I learnt in those years has enabled me to cope with what's happened to us; once you understand mental health the fear of looking after it goes away.

Fear of things makes you anxious; always work on this fact, that way you limit needless worry.

Kim, Debbie, Martin and Leo have helped out in hard times too.

I went to my new place five years ago. It has distracted me enough to see me through stressful years; it has been a job of many different hats but most have fitted because I enjoy working with people. Face to face work with service users was fantastic. Lisa and Debbie both changed me.

Yet moving into managing others, being paid to get good results by believing in people to do their job well gives me more satisfaction, and I thank the person who gave me that chance; the one who spotted my talent. And wish her well in her new "role"

I think most people I have worked with in the last years have enjoyed their time being "managed" by me. I have, for the most part, loved working with them; I have even made a few friends.

I know the following people, whether they love or hate the book, will be proud that they know I have written it…

Kevin, Paul and possibly Andy will send it back with spelling mistakes circled and demand refunds. Eve and Tracy best get all of their friends to buy it.

Other people that helped loads over the years came from a massive area; people like the original team from the place on the north coast, with its micro climate and beautiful, well located housing benefit office. Anyone that remembers Kevin banning me from his team meetings can take my love and thanks. Jess saved my life more than once.

The others from the place that has a lovely name beginning with D, In the middle of the East Riding, a beautiful part of the world. The people were warm and friendly. Anyone that remembers Julie using me to "scare" young people with can take the same.

Then the lovely generous people from all over Durham and Middlesbrough; they made me laugh and kept me going in a very difficult year for us all; shared misery was turned into a lot of laughter at that time. Many Many Thanks.

My team now had to "cope" when I was off last year at a crucial time; it's taken a long time but we are getting it together at last; solid, quality services never fail; the whole team make the service…

The better it gets the more I can thank them in person. We had a good "laugh" at our team day the other week; it is a tonic to hear people happy at work.

Now West Yorkshire and Humberside is my area and Nichola Emperoopoo, Deb, Sharon and the others help now. Even the Carrot Cake thief is useful except when she steals the cake... My travelling cup has also caused much hilarity; thanks Em!
Laughter at last in our "gang" makes work bearable again

So Thanks to everyone who has got us this far....

Thanks for the title, Soldier on

This was picked by my kid. We were discussing possibilities when this came up as a suggestion, a few days before the final draft went to the publisher. I asked why he liked it and he said it reminded him of all things to do with his Dad and the army. He went on to say that it also made him think about me last year; I must have said I needed to stop more than I thought…

The battle at that stage wasn't with my husband's illness or him as a person. I had to soldier on; fighting a battle with the local authority; a needless war to get him "looked after", the least he deserves.
We are still fighting for him to get the right treatment.

It was nearly called Tragedy, thanks to Paul O' Grady and his flippant manner. I heard him say jokingly on his show that he would use it for his Autobiography title and I thought I'd nick it, but I changed my mind for the following reason.
Wikipedia seems to be used by everyone, so I decided to look it up.
I think it could have been a tragedy but we seemed to manage to avoid it turning it into one at the eleventh hour, so we needed the name change; so Soldier On it is.

Look up "Tragedy" after you have read the book and see what you think.

Thanks for the Book

Mr White I thank you for the self belief you gave me

Emma and Mr Brown I thank you very much for the Cover, amazing what you can do with a small painting and a lot of imagination

And finally Write Books in Ferrybridge, Tom and Charlotte, Thanks.

Seven Years Bad Luck

It is the first May Bank holiday in 2007 and I am going to tell you about my bad luck over the last seven years. Just after buying the house we now live in, I bought a new mirror to be placed above the fireplace in my lovely new lounge. It had only been up for a few weeks when I heard the sound of drilling coming from next door. I went to the kitchen to get tea ready; they aren't noisy neighbours, and it was mid afternoon. I wouldn't complain. When I went back into the lounge the mirror was broken. I still wouldn't complain; I don't complain very much. I'd also say I am not really superstitious but looking back...

What did I have to be worried about? Things were going well for us; our little family of three. We both had good jobs and Dave, our son was doing ok at school. We had made a bit of profit on our first property so we had managed to move somewhere much bigger and keep our mortgage low.

We had moved to a new area and were all making new friends. I was at college upgrading my education; getting married so young had meant I had done only the basics in my teenage years. It was hard work fitting in college work within family life, but like I said it was a good time for us, our little family. The way we had planned our finances over the years meant we would probably only need to work full time for a few more years. We planned to be mortgage free be the time we were forty...
Not many people could say that at our ages.

Anyway, back to that bloody mirror. It must have been the vibrations. It wasn't an expensive mirror - eventually finding a new home at the rubbish tip after lying around uselessly in the garage. No great loss, but thinking about it, it still hasn't been replaced. Thinking about it I have spent thousands doing up this house but I have never replaced the mirror. Strange.

It was around this time; just around the start of the new millennium that my husband started to develop mental health problems. Depression, mood swings, anxiety and panic attacks, nightmares and constant issues with his self confidence and self esteem were apparent traits. His "world" had been ripped apart on leaving the army the year before. He constantly told me he felt he wasn't normal anymore; I used to wonder what he meant by that.

Now his mates were electricians, plumbers and worked in factories and shops; normal jobs. I think he meant he didn't feel "normal" compared to them. You see, the blokes he had worked with for fourteen years before now had been to war; thrown into the most hostile situations imaginable. Together they worked hard; then they drank hard. Together they were all one big, dysfunctional family. Once he'd left he felt he was alone; the Army was different from any other job on the planet and it was clear he missing some aspect of it.

He felt like the world was against him. For approximately the last four years we would describe him as being quite "mad". In the three years before that the illness just crept up slowly, but took hold. Getting worse and worse he was unable to deal with it well. As a trained soldier and strong man it was hard for him to admit he wasn't adjusting to being a "civvy". Actually being given his freedom from that regime was slowly driving him mad. All I could do was look after him and support him, persuade him to go to see the doctor. He tried, but he felt no one understood...

We have been together since we were seventeen; getting married at 18. We'd been together a year when he was posted to Germany - getting married was the only way to be together. I loved him and he loved me.
It was a match made in...

Soon it was 1991; the timing of the first "Gulf War". Both twenty one with a baby boy we were both proud of. He spent six months in a war zone; that made us both grow up pretty quickly. We both felt so much older when he got back. A few more active tours followed, he did his share in the time he spent in the army that's for sure.

Looking back it was a harsh way to have to "grow up". I was with him through thick and thin in the army and we coped with it all together; chalk and cheese, but solid. He had always looked after me. I was his precious. When he wasn't away with the Army the first fourteen years with him had been fun loving happy years. Only minor things had been thrown in our path; such as a difficult birth, but that was quickly forgotten. We both adored our little baby boy and the constant moves and separation within the Army caused a few problems, but essentially life was good.

So the mirror broke and the next five years passed. Things started to go down hill quickly after that. Eventually he had become so ill he was unable to manage in his full time job in telecoms. He walked out. He didn't want to leave. It was a good job with a large company; it paid really well, the hours were really good. He had tried asking for help and support from our Doctor, and also his work place after he had been off sick for a few weeks…

I am not joking when I say his line managers literally took the piss out of his "problem". Not understanding the illness his managers had cracked jokes about him in the yard; leaving him with no option but to leave. His post was quickly filled by one of the manager's relatives… Ironically, one of the things that had wound Rex up about his job was the nepotism within brothers, uncles, sons and various other relatives working together.

By the start of 2005 he was out of work, and extremely ill. He was determined if he could just get away from the rat race and stresses... He'd be better… Saying your life is crap is easier sometimes than admitting you have problems you need to sort out. Mortgage, kid bills, traffic jams, credit cards, family - normal life stuff other than his illness and unemployment we still had no major problems.

However, to Rex it felt like the end of the world. He just couldn't deal with any of it anymore. He truly felt, and believed our comfortable life was crap. I couldn't argue with how he felt. I could only try and keep him focused on reality; our situation wasn't the crap he clearly felt it was.

I had looked after him through five years of depression, sprinkled with manic highs when he couldn't control his emotions, crying and sobbing as much as screaming and shouting. Panic attacks had become a daily occurrence. I begged him to see the doctor. In the past I had been with him to see our GP and tried to explain to the doctor that this illness was more than the depression he had been treating Rex for. The doctor did listen, but Rex still had a problem admitting how big and life controlling the illness had got.
It was almost definitely Post Traumatic Stress. Triggered by leaving the forces and losing his network of "veterans"; people who could understand him. This diagnosis had been suggested by an assistant at our local hospital's psychiatry department some years before. I'd looked it up on the internet and collated information about it over the years.

How to seek help was the problem. It is a collection of many different illnesses; all rolled into one. It needs specialist care; the sort not readily available in our local hospital.

I know about these things. The reason being I have spent many years working with people with Mental Health Problems. The experiences have no doubt assisted me in looking after him. Over the years my training and knowledge became part of our daily life; but I couldn't "treat him". I was able to understand why he felt like he did, but I am not a psychiatrist or psychologist. I am just his wife turned full time carer.
Looking back, I was hanging around, looking after him, hoping the Old Rex, the happy, relaxed, funny, and carefree Rex would be back. On occasions we did see him, but to be honest during these pressing times he was a bit of a nightmare.

We have been going to the same place in Greece interspersed with other holidays for the last nine years. My brother has a few business dealings going on over there and we have made some good friends over the years. It's a nice place to be; very peaceful.

It had always been our plan to retire there; especially once they had built a local golf course. Rex has enjoyed the game for the last ten years. His friendship with his mate and golfing partner Mac was the only thing, apart from me and Dave that has kept him going in recent years. I should mention Mac is also ex-forces; from the same regiment…
Anyhow at least in Greece I would be able to lie on a beach while he swung a stick around hitting little balls! The sooner we could get there, the happier I would be.

We had lain on the beach for hours talking about the Greek Good life, chickens, goats; maybe even a sheep or two. Living on lovely giant tomatoes, feta cheese and fresh fish. What a way to live…

Rex decided to go out first as the advanced party. We couldn't both go but being used to separation we knew it didn't have to be the end of us. We had lived separately before; he had some work lined up, so he set off with my brother. The break in our relationship was most definitely needed; he was becoming angrier and angrier, not specifically at me but at his situation. He had very confused thoughts about many things but they always came back to his army roots. Unfortunately, it was me and Dave that were taking the blame - I didn't want to live like that anymore. We both knew life couldn't carry on the way it was; we had been so happy, but now it had become an oppressive, unhappy relationship for us both. We were both looking forward to the break.

He spent the next year back and forth between our house in England and Greece; working a bit here and there. He got by financially using the good credit he had built up from years of earning well. He missed us, but still couldn't cope with life "back here". On a daily basis he needed help to cope; every time he came home he saw our GP.

I just wanted back the man that I had known before this illness had took complete hold of his life. Watching someone you love suffering from mental distress is no different than watching them fight cancer or any other visible illness; it is heartbreaking, soul destroying and extremely hard work.

The other week at work I began talking to one of my friends, Sue. She works with people who suffer illnesses similar Rex's everyday of the week. She asked how Rex was, I responded with a flippant remark about wanting the old Rex back. Sue managed to stop me in my tracks. Leaving me speechless is something people would normally pay to see but what she said made sense.

Sue told me how she thought when people change like this the hardest thing to do would be to let the old persona go. I would have to mourn the old Rex and accept the new one. Obviously she spoke in a fashion which dressed this analysis up, using technical jargon but, essentially what she said made me think. I had been stupid; longing for someone who had gone. It made sense. I went home; looking at him with a new set of eyes. For the first time in years his illness has changed him beyond recognition; but I still loved him.

We tried to keep the decline in his health from our families and friends. This was at Rex's insistence. He didn't like the new, angry, manic, stressed, depressed person he'd become anymore than I did.
Obviously some of them knew; but couldn't help. Parts of Rex still wouldn't accept how ill he was himself. Many of them helped me; standing by me, being at the end of a phone.

To try and hide it from people he simply stopped going out and talking to people. This caused a serious problem in our social life; I was constantly making excuses to everyone, as he would agree to go somewhere or do something and then often back out on the day; often too ill to go out.

I had to stand by my man. I missed lots of parties and stuff; it was difficult. I was desperate to see friends and family but had to make do with limited access to them; going alone singled Rex out as the party pooper and I didn't want people to think that. It took a long time but I found a balance over the years; I had to leave him at home whilst I went to important social events weddings, christenings, funerals...

The reason it was hard was not physically leaving him; of course he could look after himself, I just wanted him to be well enough to come out. We had always been the life and soul of parties; it really wasn't the same without him. Rex often got upset - he wanted to go too, but was just too depressed or stressed to get out. Issues with binge drinking didn't help either to be fair.

He was back and forth for months. I went out to Greece a few times to visit. He found it hard being so far away from me but he didn't want to be dependant on me anymore; since he had let most of his friendships slip he now relied on me constantly for everything.

It was to be a new start for 2006; he seemed to be stronger in some ways. He was coping and staying calm, he had had some serious issues with anger management over the last few years but he was trying hard to keep it under control.

We talked and talked and decided we could sell the house and buy something smaller to free up cash - he could start a little business in Greece to keep us going long term.

Over the coming weeks he decided the quickest way to get the money for him to move was for me to buy our house off him. I have done ok over the years and I could just about manage financially; it stretched me more than I'd like but that's life, we have all been "stretched" like that at some stage.

So I got my own mortgage and we transferred the equity. I covered all the overspending; in the last years the size of the mortgage had doubled but there was still a healthy profit in the old pile. Now it belonged to me; safe, with a home for Dave and me. I felt a bit better. The last years had been rough and this was just a little bit of stability for us.

The line was drawn. Whatever was here belonged to me. Whatever he built in Greece belonged to him. Of course we'd still be looking after each other; separation shouldn't finish a relationship, it was just giving us both space again.

He set back off to Greece, this time taking creature comforts, including my extremely expensive music system with him... Not part of the deal we struck but then neither was the Bee Gees CD that went! He made me laugh - he's complained about listening to that CD for the 10 years since he bought it for me; then he has the front to nick it!

He'd only been there for three weeks when he had a sort of breakdown. Piecing the events together we think it started with sunstroke; he went and worked on my brother's land in 27% C heat. No hat; on a man who shaves his head...

Being blonde, fair skinned and the sun sensitive type... Having not enough water or sunscreen, he became dehydrated and began acting strangely. Our friends at the local taverna became concerned about him, as he sat eating his dinner obviously sunburnt. They thought they would see how he was the next day; he had arranged to spend the day with some of the family from the taverna.
The next day arrived and Rex set off to a family party. It was Easter; the biggest celebration of the year in Greece. He had been invited to several meals and parties by friends and this was the first one in the village. He set off walking; it was only half a mile or so. Along the way he saw an old bloke being taunted in the road by a gang of lads, he stepped in to stop it.
He has always stood up for people and would not have been able to walk by; but the gang quickly turned on Rex. He was attacked and beaten by them.

The old guy fled to a local taverna to get help but by the time people had been alerted, and started the search for him he had wandered off into the wilds; carrying an apple pie, wearing only a pair of shorts, a t-shirt and flip flops. He managed approximately 15 miles; lost on the side of a fair-sized mountain, in roasting heat. If his brain hadn't been completely cooked the day before this managed to ensure it was well done. Having been back to see our friends this year, experiencing the route he took, he was lucky he didn't die.

He claims using the setting sun, stars and such like, he found his way back. After 16 hours of being on the missing list he turned up in one of the local bars, friends started to realise how ill he was; physically and mentally, confused, beaten and then burnt to a crisp - he was ill.

Several calls later my brother was back on a flight to Greece to see what was happening out there. He had left Rex only six days ago and everything had been cool; Rex had been well settled with my sound system set up in an apartment, overlooking the sea, lucky sod…

Our Greek and English friends kept him safe for a few days and my brother flew out to Greece to bring him back. It took just over a week. Everyone agreeing that he was totally bonkers, but he didn't cause any harm or trouble, he was just ill and in need of medical attention. They flew back first on a Greek internal flight, then good old Easy Jet from Athens to UK. The flight staff were fantastic according to my brother. My friend Lisa and I drove to pick them up. Not what I had planned for the bank holiday weekend; I thought I'd be chilling out and enjoying some time alone, but if he was poorly as my brother had said and he needed to be looked after, then I had no choice. For better or worse I'd said.

He was confused about some bits of his trip but he could clearly tell us what had happened; most of which was verified by people who had seen and looked after him in the last week.

He had obviously been hit quite hard around the head; the bruising was still very visible. He had also been whipped, a long bull whip of some description. He had horrendous blisters and sores on his feet. I got him home and he seemed very settled. He was talking a lot about being a secret agent; needing to look after his family and protect us, keeping us safe.

Not surprising really, understanding what he had been through.

He'd done secret stuff in the army. We talked about it and laughed about it over the years; it was just like that really, a bit madder, confused accounts of reality is the best way to describe what he was saying... Again having worked with people who have had "mental breakdowns" I wasn't too concerned, some medication and therapy was all he needed.

After six years of having this illness he had lost the plot completely. In some ways it was a relief; he would have to get some help. The GP and the consultant at the hospital would have to listen to the facts about all of his symptoms and do something about his illness at last. But not that night, it was too late; I didn't want to be sat in A&E at this time on a Friday night.

Dave was upset about the state of his dad, worried about how poorly he was but as he helped me look after him I explained what was happening in his dad's brain. He relaxed, trusting we could help him get sorted out now.

The Brain is amazing the way it works, it is fantastic. Understanding how it can break down is interesting; learning techniques to control it can be life changing.

Looking back at last year when this happened I know why he broke down completely; he missed us. He loves us but at that stage he had given us up because he was unhappy with himself; unhappy at his insistence. I had bought the house and I think he felt like he had nothing left; I think he was trying to distract himself by being in Greece... but

We got a couple of hours of sleep. I made him poached eggs, one of his favourite breakfasts. We pottered around until it was time to drop Dave off at the cinema to meet his mates. Just after lunch we set off to our local NHS drop in; I had been to see our GP to talk about stuff before he came back, getting advice regarding what to do once Rex had got back.

The doctor there sent us to the hospital; all in all it took seven hours to get us through A&E. Loads of waiting around and having tests. Anyone in the very full waiting room would have said Rex was bonkers! We

waited in the waiting room with everyone else; he was restless and chatty but exhausted, in need of some sort of medication to slow him down. Maybe an anti- psychotic medication to slow his thoughts...
Sleep is what he needed; he'd had about 10 hours all week. My brother had slept solid since he'd got back exhausted by having to look after "Hyper Rex".
But there was no offer of treatment at the hospital. The young "Doctor" dealing with us offered to section him. I was shocked. Now, a very brief explanation of what that means. The mental health act can be used to detain people who refuse to be treated for mental health problems. This could be because they are too ill to realise they need help. This is called being detained for assessment or treatment depending which bit of the law they use. But we had been waiting in A&E for seven hours asking for help, he needed treatment for his illness, not locking up.

The young "doctor" in A&E seemed to have little experience of mental illness and was not qualified enough to issue a section (or in my opinion look after any thing bigger than a small furry animal!). I obviously questioned his decision - he started to blush. He seemed shocked to realise that I knew what he wanted to do to my husband and that I wasn't happy with it. He was asking for treatment and had done nothing to indicate he was a danger to himself or others; another criterion someone should meet if they are to be detained under the act, so why did he want to lock my husband up, I had to ask.

He kindly explained the local authority couldn't just admit him into a bed on a ward - they didn't have one; yet if they sectioned him and became "responsible" for him they would have to find him an emergency bed. The truth was they needed to lock him up to find him a bed! I told the doctor that he had a perfectly good bed at home that he could sleep in tonight. He didn't need *locking up*; it was *looking after* he needed. That is why I bought him to a hospital.
With the doctor's consent, we agreed to come back at 10am the next day. Despite being mad, Rex was clear; he wanted help to get better and there was no reason to use a section, he just needed the right treatment.

I didn't want them using this ancient act that has so many serious side effects on your life to lock my husband up; just because they couldn't offer a bed to someone suffering with his type of illness. Even with my minimal knowledge of the mental health act and I will admit I am no expert, it didn't feel like the right way to use an Act of Law; supposedly designed to protect "vulnerable people suffering mental distress". Our hospital wanted to use it to lock him up and take away his rights just because they couldn't provide a bed. Surely that's using it to cover up shortcomings in the NHS, not because Rex was refusing treatment or "lacking insight".

Everyone knows that mental health problems are very common these days, probably a lot more common than a broken leg.

Can you imagine if they offered that treatment for a broken leg; seven hour wait, no medication, no attempt to make you comfortable and then a suggestion of another three or four hours waiting to see another doctor who won't be able to fix your leg but he would authorise your detention for assessment for up to 28 days. With a promise that in that time they might not be able to fix it but they will try to get some idea how to treat it! 28 days is a long time when you're locked up.

No hospital would ever get away with that would they? But strangely they do in the case of "Mental Illness".

We turned back up the next day as planned, just after 10am. We faced more waiting around. Four hours later, the young doctor who was still on duty managed to find a "suitable" bed.

I hung around for quite a while helping to get him settled, answering all of the questions they asked about him; his problems and any risks with him. I told them everything; I think I was a bit relieved after living with it and coping alone for all that time; I just wanted them to look after him.

We got him settled into his room; it was grim but that was the only option they offered and he needed help. He was ill; physically and mentally. I knew he needed medical help, I didn't want to leave him but I had no choice.

I popped home to have some food with Dave; he'd been neglected since his Dad came back and he was slap bang in the middle of his final exams at school. His options at college depended on his grades resultant of these exams.

We ate our dinner and tried to chill out. It was about two hours since I'd left Rex at the hospital when I decided to ring and check he was ok. The nurse that answered informed me he was getting wound up. When I asked what about he became vague, not answering my questions. Eventually I asked if I should come down to try and help chill him out. The nurse said I could try. He seemed distracted and couldn't tell me what was wrong. Rex had only been there a short time. I jumped in my car and arrived within 15 minutes. Within 30 minutes I had witnessed him being restrained and shackled face down like a criminal for allegedly pulling a radiator of a wall and threatening to kill the Psychiatrist - Allegedly ...

Let me just recap; he had been ill for all those years, attacked and beaten as well as suffering sunstroke and severe dehydration over the last week.

He had been looked after in Greece by friends, bar owners, travel reps, Greek joiners and Fishermen. Oh and I best not forget Wayne and John good friends of my brother; you have to trust me when I tell you those three definitely never met at nursing school... But between them they looked after him for a week...Followed by a four hour flight with easy jet staff looking after him; my brother who is no Florence Nightingale had been his nurse for the last days he'd been safe and looked after.

It was a four hour journey from the airport; Rex had then he'd been at home with me and Dave for nearly two days and yes that's right just three hours in a hospital with trained staff and Psychiatrists looking after him in a NHS hospital.

The restraint was done by four burly riot police with shields and mace at the ready… I had worked in environments like this for years and I had never seen someone taken with such brute force. Even people who had been dangerous and had extremely aggressive and violent backgrounds due to their illnesses had never been carried out of wards like this where I'd worked.

I must be honest in saying that I have never ventured much into the NHS; this must be the low standards expected by our local authority. I have worked mainly in private hospitals and now for a charity; the sorts of places that tend to teach you to respect everyone you work with. This was the most undignified thing I had ever witnessed happen to someone; that is without throwing in the fact that it had just happened to an extremely ill man that I love.

Rex had no history of physical aggression. Before he went off to Greece the first time he had become a shouter; verbally aggressive. That was the reason we had got to the end of the road living together; I hate shouting, always have but like I said before in the last year since he had been back and forth between us and Greece he had calmed down quite a bit. In the days since the attack he had been up and down a bit at first but then calm and very funny; the extreme change to super chilled which was what he was when I left him at the hospital was part of my reason for taking him in the first place.

I had told the staff at the hospital the truth; I understand risk assessing. I work in an environment where I have to prioritise staff safety on a daily basis and never in twenty years have I witnessed him being physically aggressive to anyone except me - we have had what I would call scraps but no one else. I would have told them if there was any danger but honestly I didn't think there was any danger for them in looking after him, but they obviously felt differently to have got him taken away like this.

I trusted them to look after my husband and they had failed to do it. I pointed this out and as I left the ward I called the staff some choice names and made some threats of my own; amazingly they didn't call the police in to restrain me!!!

So May bank holiday last year was spent with him locked in police cells. The nurse told me they had taken him to a place of safety as they couldn't look after him safely at the hospital. So why hadn't they offered him medication the night before so I could have then looked after him at home?

Whilst locked up in that police cell they detained him under the mental health act. All human rights removed, no rights to visitors, solicitors, or anyone else that isn't appointed by the health authority. Eventually they took him to a new "suitable" bed after keeping him locked up for 19 hours; the only problem was he'd had no care or treatment for all that time.

I could imagine what state he was in. The last time I saw him he was being carried along a corridor face down with no shoes on his feet. I prayed he was ok. I don't know why I prayed; I am not religious but it would take a bloody miracle for him to survive being treated like that.

I had spent the time he was locked up arguing with social workers and NHS managers. It was ridiculous; I was in a complete state; I rang several people in the night to get advice. As his "next of kin" I was helpless. They were looking after him, or so they said but they weren't looking after him remember, the police were.

The suitable bed was a two hundred and twenty mile round trip for me but the local authority weren't bothered; as it turned out they never sent anyone to see him.

The police eventually transferred him to the hospital and to be fair they had been the most helpful professionals that I'd had contact with in the last twenty four hours. They had seemed worried about him too...
I contacted the hospital direct. God knows why it took so long to get the blooming bed; it only took me two minutes to find the hospital on the internet and it was just as quick to pick up the phone. I wanted to know what sort of place it was.

25

I was put through to Gordon, the nurse in charge. He managed to calm me down by promising to look after Rex; laughing at me as I told him that he would need plenty of water as he would be seriously dehydrated. It had been a scorching weekend; he had been seriously ill and locked up for the last day. I couldn't stop talking. I was so worried. It got to a point when I instructed him to make sure Rex was fed. Gordon stopped me; he told me straight he had been trained to look after people and had known about the need to feed patients for sometime now; he thought they could manage it.

Had I been stood in a room with him it would have been one of those classic moments when someone gets slapped around the face to calm them down!
He basically told me at this point to calm down, get some sleep; pointing out the anxiety and stress I had been through in the last hours. I was all for getting in my car and driving over to the hospital. Gordon replied he wouldn't let me in till lunchtime the next day.

Now my luck was changing. I could hear warmth in his voice that I trusted. Lisa turned up to help; we ate pizza and distracted Dave for the rest of the day. I slept a little and worried a lot.

The next day we got up and went straight over to the hospital arriving just before lunchtime. It was a bit of a long haul but straight forward enough; we went round one roundabout twice!

The original tests in A&E had uncovered a slight trace of cannabis in his urine; not that surprising really. We had occasionally smoked a little weed on trips to Amsterdam and at parties over the years but had never caused problems other than fights over things like munchie food. I remember one night a debate starting over the fair sharing of a trifle and a few little disagreements over which flavour crisps to eat but "Drug induced Psychosis" had never been witnessed. I also knew whatever he had smoked in Greece would have been very low grade stuff compared to what we had in Dam.

We openly discussed this with the staff at the hospital; our local hospital had tagged his illness "Drug Induced Psychosis" from the start of this book I want to make my attitude towards the use of Cannabis clear, having lived and worked with PEOPLE for most of my life with substance abuse issues, the use of cannabis for grown up consenting adults is no worse or better than the use of alcohol for the same purpose, to relax and chill out at appropriate times. Overuse of anything is what causes problems. Using either to cover a mental health problem is wrong but that's what happens when treatment isn't available for people.

Over the weeks he was being assessed under his section the opinion appeared to be that this was a lot more than just a temporary period of drug induced psychosis as suggested by our hospital. The doctors here seemed to think it was PTSD too.

It was a fantastic place; they treated his physical problems and monitored his mental health. For the most part they appeared to agree he had been suffering from this illness for a long time; all of the staff took time to talk to him about himself, his past and his problems; keeping him focused on getting the right treatment for his illness and moving his life forward.

He talked to the staff there at length about wanting to sort his health problems out; I liaised with our own GP and contacted the charity Combat Stress. I even managed to get a referral to a clinic at the private hospital where I had been previously employed after hearing about a specialist in the treatment of PTSD.

Life was calming down again at last after the trauma of his attack. He was lucky he hadn't blooming well died in Greece. Then the trauma of his hospital visit and detention in a police cell; he had been through a lot in the last few weeks. After 23 days on a section two; being cared for and assessed at a good hospital they let him come home. He had been described by staff as being a little confrontational over being "locked up" in the first few days but had been easily distracted; they had agreed that he did have problems and needed treatment.

They certainly agreed with me; he didn't need to be detained to force him to get treatment. They had got to know him well and all believed that he would take help from anywhere it was offered. They had spent twenty four hours a day with him for twenty three days.

Our own local authority didn't seem interested in looking after him, originally saying he would be out of our area for a week at the most; it ended up being three and a half weeks. I rang them daily in the last week he was in the hospital in Waterloo; asking them to sort out some treatment for him. At one stage the matron or whatever the evil witch was called practically called me a liar and told me Rex wouldn't be coming home that soon; her staff at the hospital had told her how "mad and aggressive" he was; it was a joke.

By this stage I was going to pick him up the next day after the ward round; the day when all of the professionals that had looked after him would meet and agree that he needed treatment for PTSD, not detaining in a hospital, I trusted them and their judgement.

By my calculation the total cost of his assessment at that private hospital must have cost our local health authority in the region of thirty thousand pounds. He had cat scans and every test known to man as well as a lot of time with various Psychiatrists and Psychologists. Music Therapy and Occupational therapy was enjoyed; he liked being kept busy as well as one to one nursing. They had paid well to determine and diagnose what was wrong with him, but they still couldn't offer him any treatment. He didn't need a lot of some medication, an hour or two with some sort of therapist that's all he needed; probably fifty quid tops a week for a little while to help him get better.

We got home and life settled down again. During his stay in hospital we had teased him about thinking he was a Greek God. To be fair he was looking quite well; he had lost a few pounds and getting himself a fantastic tan by frying himself (and his brain!) in the weeks he had been in Crete. It had made him look well.

He was full of energy; planning on doing loads of jobs, his mind was still wandering a bit but he was doing ok. It was Tuesday and the weekend was to be the second bank holiday in May. I knew I could get through the week by believing that it could not be as bad as the last. I had booked an appointment with our GP to get Rex's prescription for his sleeping pills; the Community Mental Health Team should be coming in to sort it out but since it was the only medication he had been given and I didn't want to be without them with the holiday weekend coming up, I booked the appointment as a back up.

What he really needed was support in the community but it certainly didn't look like he was going to get any before the weekend.

I did contact the Community team and the hospital direct on Wednesday but on Thursday we were at the emergency back up appointment with our GP, the prescription was done and he assured us that someone from the Community Mental Health team would be in touch soon. We had been home two days and they hadn't been in touch yet...

By Friday he was struggling to cope; he felt like he was stressing me out because I had to look after him again. When he was in hospital he had kept promising me I wouldn't have to look after him anymore; he was going to get better. After hours of trying to convince him that all was ok, it would just take time. Towards tea time, I asked what he wanted to do. It was his choice on what to do; he was talking about going back to the hospital.

He said he wanted to go back to the hospital to give me a break, I contacted them at Waterloo and they said they would take him back as long as we took him straight in. They had said to contact them if we had any problems; I knew they would help. They told me to ring NHS direct to talk to a doctor locally about funding.

I contacted our health authority; the on call GP that spoke to me agreed that he should go back to the same hospital. With the recent events it would definitely be the best option for him. Unfortunately he called back a little later and said I would have to bring him back to our local hospital, they wouldn't fund another stay at the original hospital; they wouldn't even send a doctor to see him at home. I would have to bring him back to A&E.

I didn't think it was really a good option, after the last visit only weeks earlier I had no choice but to try to support him through this at home. My friend Lisa had been round helping me sort stuff out. I told her to go home; no point hanging around. We thought we would be taking him back to hospital.

To be honest I was getting tired out by this stage; he was starting to say quite bizarre things again. Three days is too long to wait; they knew what his symptoms were but they had done nothing to start his treatment. Because they had used a section two they had only paid for him to be assessed, it was up to the local authority to treat him; it was madness.

I got him in the bath; this had been helping to chill him out over the last few weeks. I thought a bath and then try and get him to sit and watch TV for an hour, administrating sleeping tablets before bed and everything would be ok for the night.

I jumped in as he got out, I had only been in the bath a few minutes when he started shouting at me from upstairs; he had logged onto the internet and started reading stuff about Greek gods. He was shouting at me about all sorts of stuff. I got a wash and got out of the bath grumpily; I just wanted to relax and chill out. I threw on my old, holey dressing gown, my hair still stuck in my headband. He came rushing down the stairs, started rambling on about cutting a baby out of a womb. God only knows what he'd been reading up there but as I went to sit down he flipped the small sofa over. He was on the other side of the room; he didn't even look at me, he then started cutting the bottom of it with a veg knife.

I calmly stood back up grabbed my phone and left, I rang 999. I thought they would send something; maybe a police car or ambulance. I told them everything as I walked down the street and hid behind a post box. I waited there for 25 minutes; my neighbours walked passed walking their dogs, saying their good evenings like seeing a woman in her dressing gown hiding behind a post box is an every day occurrence.

Eventually a policeman turned up and told me to get in his car. A few minutes later he told me to get into the van that had just pulled up alongside. I spoke with a young police man called Max; telling all the stuff I told them about his illness appeared to matter less than the fact that he was an ex soldier with PTSD who was cutting up my sofa with a veg knife because he was bonkers; once again I tried to explain to them that he wasn't really dangerous. If they could just let me speak to him.

It wasn't me talking to him but a trained negotiator; it turned into a two and a half hour armed siege around my house. I think the neighbours enjoyed it; I certainly didn't. Having to answer questions like "have you got any guns, swords machetes and such like?" Who did they think we were? I had told them we are a normal family with an ill man, why they wouldn't listen I don't know.

As you can imagine I had all sorts running through my head, not to mention worrying about Dave, out at his end of school party… I was probably as near to having a heart attack as I could be! I was so stressed again. The last weeks of having him assessed had been for nothing. What would happen to him this time? I even had thoughts of him being shot by mistake running through my head.

It turned out that he had calmed down quickly and rang our friend Sharon, who lives round the corner to see if I had gone there. That's why it had taken so long to get him out of the house; he had rang her as my phone was constantly engaged, remember I had been on the 999 call for 25 minutes.
He had left several messages on my phone clearly showing that he had calmed himself down. It haunts me now. Why did I panic? It all happened in 10 minutes tops; but I was tired and at the end of my energy reserves. Again I thought the authorities would help us out by looking after him; this time it was spectacular…

In the end he walked out of the house with no problem; but it was back to a police cell not a hospital. This time they used a section three

- this should be used to admit people to hospital that are refusing treatment but once again this hadn't been the case again; we had both been begging for help.

This time it took them a staggering 20 hours to find him a bed, they had him locked up in a police cell whilst using a law which states he should be in a hospital being treated!

Their standards of care and treatment whilst they had him locked up in a cell fell well below what I think an old soldier deserves; especially when his madness was triggered from the time he was fighting for queen and country, fighting a war that was definitely over oil and not people, way back in the nineties when no one was interested in Saddam, only the Politics and Oil. That's when the can of worms was opened and Saddam's "terrorist army" started gathering strength according to some people ...

This time the suitable bed was local, just a mere 90 mile round trip.

Once again he was cuffed and transported again; it had taken four weeks for the wounds on his wrists to heal from the last time they restrained him like this; even today the scars are still quite bad.

Unfortunately, I didn't get the same warm feeling that they had provided me in Waterloo this time; we got the number off the internet and gave them a ring.

I asked about coming to see him and they informed me that I would need to book a visiting time for the next day. It turned out this place was like a prison; they allowed three, one hour visiting slots each afternoon for the whole ward, there was about sixteen patients on that ward as it turned out if everyone got visitors they could get one and a half visits a week but they didn't do half's... And they are supposed to be patients in a hospital not prisoners.

Trying to see Rex became a battle, no booking appointments whilst you were there, and they were extremely good at cutting you off on the phone when you rang through. Much less visiting time was allowed than last time; medical evidence suggests that patients with regular visitors and support recover much quicker than those without, but that wasn't a concern at this place. Within a week the approved "doctor" at this place had clearly told me and Rex that they wouldn't be starting any treatments other that drug treatment. They had been told he wouldn't be there long enough to start any therapy so they wouldn't bother starting any treatment, they just started medicating.

Again I questioned the decision; he was being held under an act that is used to "force treatment" for those who need it and refuse to accept it. Due to the fact that he had been asking for treatment and now they were saying he wouldn't be getting any, Rex questioned the reasons they had for keeping him locked up.

She did agree he needed therapy but was very clear they wouldn't be offering it at this place. They kept saying Rex wouldn't be there that long, our local authority said about a week again.

This time it took six weeks and a solicitor to get him out of that shit hole they had the front to call a hospital. Once a "doctor" has declared that you are mad enough to detain only they can sign the paperwork to let you go; the criteria you must meet in order to be detained in this way is to be a danger to yourself or others or you "lack insight" into what your problems are, neither applied to him. Like I said he is quite mad and definitely not dangerous…

They soon disliked me at that "hospital". I made sure I booked a visiting slot every day; my husband was in hospital ill, not a prisoner. I also took other friends and family in with me. I knew I may need independent witnesses to verify some of the things I saw there. If people involved in his care denied incidents that were happening to him in their care, such as incidents of over medication (he was off his face for the first week). On several occasions one specific nurse made the same mistake several times; he was given medication that wiped him out, making him unable to move, having to lay on his bed for hours to give the side effects of the medication time to pass.

Rex was finding this very distressing as he was not in control of himself they were knocking him out, scary for anyone I should imagine.

They made him sleep on the floor for three nights like a dog to "teach him how to behave himself". Oh, and best of all they wouldn't let anyone under the age of 18 visit, resulting in Dave not being able to see his dad for six weeks. If I booked weeks in advance with the "social worker" they could have a supervised 30 minute meeting in a secure room. I asked Dave and Rex if they wanted me to sort it out for them to see each other but they said sod that…

It is up to the hospital to organise an independent panel to listen to Rex's case; the only right of a patient in this vulnerable situation is to put their faith in someone supporting them to present information to an independent panel to get the decision to keep them locked up overturned; it took six weeks for the hospital to arrange it.

At the "hearing" it didn't take long for the three panel members to make a decision; that he could not be detained any longer under the mental health act. They were detaining him on the recommendation of one doctor even though many people had commented he didn't need locking up in the last months; including some of the nursing staff at this hospital. They weren't all bad, but they were all intimidated by the management to some extent.
It was at this exact moment as the panel said he was free to go that the hospital receptionist interrupted the panel hearing to say our local hospital could offer him a bed…

Even the social worker they had sent to the panel from our local authority was embarrassed that they had offered so little, so late in the day.

Excuse my French but this time I thought bollocks to that, again for the six weeks he'd been in hospital I begged them to move him closer, to allow more relaxed visiting and to get him into an environment that was more suitable; where his treatment could start but they hadn't offered anything.

34

The last eleven weeks had cost me over a grand in petrol just to visit him not to mention the exhaustion I was suffering driving those long distances to visit him.

As well as trying to support our kid through this important time in his life, taking his exams, laying his foundations for the future... It was him I felt most sorry for in all of this. The timing was extremely bad. Again that is life, but sometimes it is hard. No kid should have to watch this happen to their parent, let alone in the middle of their sixteenth summer when life should be cool, finishing school and moving on...

The stress they had put me through failing to treat his illness appropriately resulted in me having to take three months off work. I had spent every penny I had and they offered him a bed because they couldn't pay to keep him locked up anymore. I wish I had thousands of pounds to spend like our local authority seemed to have...
I wonder if it eased their conscience paying a private hospital to lock him up; you know out of sight out of mind. If he was locked up miles away then they didn't have to look after him.
.

There's a lot more later on in the book so I won't go on but they made me very angry! But once again I took him home to look after him; I needed to get sorted; I had to get back to work or we would all end up homeless...
Returning to the weekend of the mirror incident. I only remembered the mirror the other day; I am superstitious and I had forgotten about it but, looking back over the last seven years since it smashed, I am hoping that this is the end of my run of "bad luck" and that it may have had something to do with what's been happening.

In all honesty I believe that you make your own luck, but you know those days when it doesn't matter how hard you try everything still goes wrong? You get up on time; but then you stub your toe in the shower, miss the bus, lose your keys, spill your first coffee, offend your boss... you know the days I mean.

If it was the mirror and the bad luck thing then the seven years is up, thank god! The last seven years have been crazy and I always thought about writing a book, so when this happened to Rex, me and Dave I knew I would have to write it down in a bid to try and tell this story, as I know there are loads more stories like ours out there. And it isn't right that ill people are treated like this, the added fact that Rex is a War Veteran in my mind makes it worse.

It just took time to decide how to start and end it; I even struggled along the way with whose story it is to tell.

But eventually I have worked it out realising I just had to tell the truth. That is how I live my life on a daily basis and believe in telling the truth; it hardly ever gets you into trouble.

If I am honest, nine months later, looking after Rex is still a full time job, the aspects of his illness such as his lack of motivation, self esteem and confidence are an issue. As well as suffering from bouts of depression that he was managing to control without medication.

The whole of this is being impounded by still being over medicated for his "mood swings". Making his moods immovable; he can't get angry because the medication is suppressing that emotion to make him "safe" to live in the community. But at the same time it stops him from being happy. That is a massive barrier to overcome in terms of getting him well; if he can't feel anything, how can he deal with his problems?
He is still not getting any treatment or therapy other than medication from the NHS, all these months later.

The consultant who has been responsible for him since he was discharged from hospital has offered no help. He has asked me to sort out the things that cause Rex stress; for instance, his debt and other things, but that has not helped Rex's dependency on me at all. But with no one else offering to help him out I have had to carry on doing everything for him. He wants to be in control of his own life but he needs help.

The only other thing the consultant has done for Rex was manage to fill in a simple form incorrectly for the DVLA towards the back end of last year; he ticked all the wrong box's resulting in them revoking Rex's driving licence for 3 years. A simple mistake he says…

Another mistake by the NHS that caused unnecessary stress to my husband and family; they really just don't seem to care. Looking after someone with serious anxiety issues would surely mean that some care is taken over those sorts of things, losing your licence at any stage is traumatic, let alone when you have done nothing to warrant it.

I was actually at the hairdressers when he opened the letter from the DVLA informing him of the decision. He was hyperventilating down the phone; Dave had to sit with him until I got back. I was having my roots done and having met the consultant I was sure it was a mistake. I reassured him down the phone, he was extremely stressed but he'd have to cope for an hour until my roots had cooked.

The letter was quite strong. It said the licence was to be immediately revoked. It took weeks and numerous letters for me to get this stupid mistake sorted out; all because his doctor made a mistake…

I had also managed to get him some private therapy with the help of SSAFA, a charity dealing with Service personnel kindly paid for it.

It helped him a lot. The psychologist understood him and helped him work through his issues. After twelve sessions he was doing well; he made me laugh as he came home from his last session telling me that with positive thinking he could control his illness; he just needed to practice doing it.

The twelve hundred quid it cost was money well spent. A lot more value for money than the possible sixty thousand that our local authority spent on "looking after" him i.e. by locking him up.

We are I am sure, over the worst of it and if I sell this book maybe other people might not have to go through this whether they are War

Veterans deserving better or mad folk asking for help. No one deserves to go through weeks of being locked up and treated like this trying to get help for any illness. Again imagine the outcry if a broken leg hadn't been fixed after a year...

We have survived again and the offers of work in Greece are still there so maybe in the future we can move on.

He is much better and he wants to come off his medication; move on. Maybe he could do with a little more therapy to keeping him ticking over, but he does understand his illness at last. That at least makes it easier to live with him.

He needs to get out more too. Oh yeah he also needs to find a job, anyone needing an honest, trustworthy, funny, well qualified telecom engineer can call.... He is mad but aren't we all!

The rest of the book tells the story of us, how we met, how we survived and what made us who we are. We are really just a normal family. You might know us; we may be your neighbours. You might have worked with us or met us in the past. You may know one, two or all three of us; but I am sure whether you know us or not you will think that parts of this story are unbelievable, but it is the truth.

Towards the end of the book the details of his treatment are not meant to offend everyone. I will acknowledge at this stage that a few individuals within our local health service and the more local hospital were very good; but unfortunately the services offered by them were horrendous and I can't lie. No offence is meant or should be taken.

At the same time I would say that the good people at Waterloo should take every bit of praise that's been offered, and a very big thank you for all they did.

Who's Who

So as you have gathered my husband is ex-forces and I manage a staff team for a charity giving support to vulnerable people in the community. Last year I managed 22 different schemes for people with mental health problems, learning difficulties, offenders, homeless, young people to name but a few. I run supported houses for young people; a client group I have always avoided but enjoyed it immensely.

Over the past four years my crew and I have supported thousands of people. I love the place I work in; the people are good and the work very rewarding. Making a difference to people's lives is the best job, not the easiest. Real people often in chaotic situations such as homeless and/or drug and alcohol dependant make each day different and challenging. Staff teams in places like ours are often made up from hard working, caring, and dedicated, often-strong people from all kinds of backgrounds. People who do this job often do it for satisfaction rather than massive salaries; this makes them passionate about the job which can make them difficult to manage, said with a smile on my face…

It's never dull, no two days are the same and it pays the bills.

I am one of those independent women. As you have probably guessed I earn my own money, own my own house and car. I work hard. I'm 37 (real time writing this book I have now turned 30 frikin 8) and feel a bit like Bridget Jones having a mid-life crisis; except in my case life has been complicated by a man for twenty years; interesting, funny, happy years but definitely complicated. I have been a good wife to Rex and a good mum to my beautiful sixteen-year-old son, Dave.

Unfortunately though, like Bridget I think I am in the middle of a mid-life crisis. One which is being kept at bay only by a nervous breakdown. So my big pants are actually keeping me held together, not sucking in my wobbly bits. I like the Bridget Jones films. I often laugh at my own stressful days the way I laugh at her films; often there is nothing you can do to stop the bad things that happen, so what is the point getting in a flap?

You will have also realised by now that we have had a few bad months with Rex's illness but it hasn't always been doom and gloom. He is a lovely man; I have been his wife for nearly 20 years. It's only over the last years he has developed post traumatic stress disorder. It has been a progressive illness, starting just after his time ended in the army. There was an incident a few months before he left the army but at the time I put that down to drink. Put your hand up if you have never been stroppy after having a drink?

Nightmares, mood swings, manic highs lasting from hours to days, followed by periods of bad depression, followed by shouting; it's a terrible illness; anxiety and panic have ruled his life.
I love him. After twenty years with someone there is a lot of love. But we couldn't live together with his madness anymore; with us both at the end of our tether. Rex had tried to get help for his illness but there had never been enough help offered so we decided we had to separate for a while, hence his trips to Greece.

This part of the book describes our meeting and the years that followed. It's been a good life. We are chalk and cheese in many ways but as it's worked for long enough we must have something good. I have always been a little mad; I think it came from my early years. I am out spoken and prone to fooling about, trying to make people laugh, all my friends have funny laughs; I find it always brightens the day.

Rex on the other hand has always been solid and dependable, loyal. He's always chosen fewer friends than I, but usually results in having stronger relationships with the chosen few than I have with my friends. He is quite shy and not very talkative, unless he is in company that is familiar to him; he's very funny in a dry, quiet sort of way.

Over the last years I have learnt a lot about mental health and behaviours. I know you might think I am mad, but I truly believe you have to understand mental health to be able to look after yourself; a bit like checking your breasts or testicles for cancer, visiting the dentist to check your teeth; we are taught about checking this stuff but no one tells you how to look after your mental health.

The biggest issue with mental health problems is that it is in your head so people can't see it or measure how bad it is. As it is not an exact science it is hard for anyone to help. You have to learn to look after yourself. You know that old saying when you are having a bad day, pick yourself up, dust yourself off and get on with it? Well that's what I believe, you have to, only you can control your thoughts. If people are really "mad" they might need medication but mostly you have to sort out what the problem is and do something, anything to put it right.

Real treatments, like talking therapies and practical therapies to help people aren't easy to get on the NHS. I do not want to offend anyone with any associated illness I may describe in this book by belittling or making light of these serious illnesses but I have to be light about it or it could stress me out and drive me mad.

I have sometimes got a bit fed up, but never thought about whether it is depression or some other "illness"; yet I suppose my doctor was right last year whilst it was all going on with Rex; I was off work, she diagnosed me with reactive depression. It seemed to last for about six weeks whilst I was under extreme pressure.

When I think back now had things like losing my parents, my mum at 13 and my dad at 30, constant moves in the army, stress giving birth to my baby, a car crash that could have killed me, and a long term illness that ended up with a botched operation in an army hospital caused periods of reactive depression in the past? I just always believed I was fed up because stuff happens; it is called life. I am a realist and life can't always be good. Human nature dictates that when bad things happen you feel like crap; it is only the degree of unhappiness that varies. If you stub your toe you may well be unhappy for a minute or two, if one of your parents dies that unhappiness can go on for weeks or years.

Being diagnosed now puts me down as a statistic; you know one in four adults have mental health problems. I am now officially one of them; oh no my poor child growing up with two mad parents…

I can assure you no children or animals have been hurt or injured in the making of this book; Dave is a well balanced, lovely, lazy teenager... He isn't an angel but he is good, kind and very easy going.

I had a proud moment last week when I had a group of friends round. After several bottles of wine, a heated discussion around politics and religion ensued...asylum, terrorism, you know the sort of debate... Dave sat listening; nursing his one can of Carlsberg. Yes I do take a responsible approach to his drinking; two or three cans, safe at home with us. He is by now 17; it will soon be to late to teach him about hangovers and the demon drink because he'll be old enough to do what he wants. I prefer pro-active parenting; letting him have a hangover after a family party at sixteen had seen his attitude towards drink change drastically; he was put off drinking to excess quite nicely. This makes going to parties and music gigs easier to control; I know for the most part when he is out he is being sensible about what he is drinking.

Anyway back to the night, just as one friends eyes went dark as she prepared to jump up and kill another friend, Dave stopped us all in mid sentence by telling us it didn't matter about religion or politics; it is about individuals.
He then went on to explain to us oldies; extremists come in all shapes and forms, Blair, Bush, Hussein all featured on his extensive list. We all sat; transfixed as he silenced, making us think he was up to the point when Jordan was also classed extremist for the size of her boobs; even then we could understand the point he was trying to make. We are Katie Price fans in our house; Rex and Dave like her for obvious reasons, I like the fact that she is a normal working woman; wife, mother and all round nice person. I don't know her personally but that's the feeling I get. Anyway he turned the simmering pot of politics and religion back into a light hearted conversation. All of my friends were impressed by his understanding of the world; he was on a winner. As he laughed his head off taking a picture of Sharon my mate, his mates mum, in a less than sober state dancing around our living room quite drunk, to use as blackmail evidence at a later date... The internet and myspace have an awful lot to answer for!

So it seems we, two mad parents couldn't have done a bad job, he's a balanced young adult with a good outlook on life (and a photo of his mates mum to make money on when it turns up on his "space" on the web!) He is a well adjusted seventeen year old; even if I do say so myself.

Surrounded by good friends and family he copes well in his little mad family. I manage to control my depression, stress and anxiety by using "mind over matter skills". He would tell you that he has good support from me; we get by quite happily but the facts are both of his parents have "issues".

The other thing we have found over the last few years is that he certainly isn't alone. A few of his friends families have problems like ours; in some cases worse, some better but there are certainly a lot of wobbly, mad families out there.

My family is massive. I am the youngest of six natural siblings, but we have stepbrothers and sisters all over. I was born in 1969; the baby in the family of three sisters and two brothers. My mum was a very strong woman emotionally; I remember she had a very strong personality. She also managed to survive her heart stopping twice for long periods whilst under general anaesthetic; this was the early seventies when most people that had heart attacks died. She never fully recovered physically but even a dodgy ticker took years to kill her. By the time I was old enough to start having clear memories of her she was more or less using a wheelchair all the time; disabled by her conditions. My dad was an alcoholic business man.

Life was quite hard for my family. In my earliest years my dad could comfortably support us financially, but spent most of it on drink. Verbal and physical abuse was normal in our house. Around the age of two I remember seeing my dad stab my mum. Domestic violence wasn't even a crime in those days. Human rights and Protection from abuse was never even discussed back then; it was just the way people lived a lot of the time.

All those things that we take for granted now; we all expect to be accepted in every day life no matter who we are, and the intolerance of any sort of abuse has stamped out a lot of the problems. But we all know that I am not the only person on the planet who had a start in life like that.

During my early years I remember my mum was often called names such as "spaz" and "mong". We used to get bullied for pushing her round in a wheelchair.
God forbid you would take out a woman in a wheelchair in the seventies.

She actually had a heart condition and arthritis. No mobility but no evil, contagious, outrageous illness that meant she couldn't safely go out in a wheelchair.
If you had to use a wheelchair in the seventies the names I have mentioned were used because people had yet to realise just because your legs didn't work didn't mean that your brain automatically didn't work. That is what it was like back in "those days". I am sure most people meant no maliciousness in the use of these names, or in their lack of understanding of my mother's problems. But I am glad that these attitudes have been challenged and changed over the last decades.

We lived in a big city. My dad owned boarding houses; they were full of Blacks, Asians and Irish; many colourful people. It may sound strange to mention this but we would often be teased because of the people that lived with us! During the 70's, in most towns and cities in Britain, most people except white, British, able bodied people were discriminated against to some extent. Life could be difficult for anyone who was different; however we did have blacks and Irish and anyone else that needed a place to live. Over the years I realised my mum was too kind and caring to turn anyone away and my dad would let anyone in as long as they paid rent.

There was even my Auntie Mary; I believed she was my auntie until discovering a few years ago during half of a conversation with my sister that Mary was definitely a he before he became my "Auntie".

The two blokes that lived together in the house next door; "the queers" as my mum would cal them in the most affectionate way; all made interesting first years for me...

This all shaped how we perceived people; being bought up to believe that every person has the same value despite what people looked like; the colour of skin, sexuality and affluence paid no part in my mum's acceptance of people. Years later I can honestly say that the packaging of people is irrelevant to me; I think it makes life much easier. Worrying if people are better or worse than ourselves for any reason takes up valuable brain space that can be used for other things.

All the people that lived with us got paid weekly; they'd all bring us sweets and presents on a Thursday; we'd get them whilst my parents got the rent.

If other people chose to look down their noses at people for any reason that was their choice, but in our house everyone was equal except my dad, he was an extremely drunk "GOD".

People are precious in life, and without exception I have always tried to decide for myself if I like people or not. It is ok to dislike someone as long as it is the person within you don't get along with; nothing to do with looks or possessions. Wrappings on a person are even less important to me than wrappers on chocolate bars; much less important to be honest, chocolate wrappers get in the way of eating chocolate for a few minutes.

Being shouted at in the street and having abuse thrown at me because our mum was in a wheelchair was a daily occurrence. I often smiled even as a kid; she was a large, outrageous and loud woman that people loved; she was a proper old cockney.

She would often embarrass people who assumed she couldn't speak because she was in a wheelchair by saying something witty; that would often endear her to most people that she met.

From my upbringing I learnt many lessons; one of the most important was to be tolerant. Accepting and possibly on the downside a little

45

submissive; she did shout a lot to make up for the fact that her legs didn't work. She'd have been the fastest woman on the planet if she could have moved her chair with the hot air from her mouth.

I don't think I am alone though, many of us 70's babies have these traits.

Accepting and submissive; this is what kids were as we moved into the eighties; the law was still respected and rules were only broken a little bit...
The boundaries of society weren't seriously pushed until the start of the 90's rebel. Binge drinking and drug abuse moved into everyday mainstream life, at the same time as the nanny state kicked in, curbing punishment and control of society.

We people of a certain age just missed it all; by then we were all growing up and doing the usual stuff, like having families, getting dogs, paying mortgages, getting stressed etc, etc.
Apart from that lucky bitch Bridget Jones. I wonder what she was doing in the eighties; having a ball at university probably. I think she was really lucky to be a spinster....

Looking back, it seems like I was bought up on an Alien planet. But I am sure that was more to do with the seventies than my family. It seems to me some level of what we would term today as abuse; physical or mental, was present in a lot of homes in the seventies. Discipline was the key in most families. Smacking your kids was more than normal; it was expected. Family and Family life were sacred. Family stuck together. Most people came from decent sized families that were clearly linked by marriage and extended beyond belief, but they seemed to make up sizeable units during the seventies.

During the eighties, the 'Domestic family' became the way forward; less big families, 2.4 children became the norm. People started becoming more materialistic; allowing less money for big families and lots of kids; preferring to spend their spare money on big cars and houses. This was fast becoming more important in society than family values. Using your money to show off instead of supporting big families was becoming the "norm". Having possessions seemed to take priority over having family.

By the early eighties, and the onset of my teenage years, it was starting to become clear that the picture of domestic family life was changing; now people were encouraged to have two children, two cars, maybe a dog... Many people outside of this ideal were being classed as outside of the "perfect family". Bearing in mind most people already came from big families; more or less overnight many people left the realms of being big families to being outcast "large problem families". In a lot of cases this started to criminalise these families; who often worked hard but lived on "housing estates" the issues and ripples of which we still read and hear on the news about today.
Although my family situation was still strange, having a mum in a chair never got any easier in her lifetime; unfortunately it was at this time that easier divorces and loss of social divides between cultures within the country began to change family units.
Many more people came from less than perfect families, but that was ok by me because it meant that I blended in more. Having a disabled mother could be checked off against having divorced parents in the "normality" stakes back then.

I don't think the picture of the family norm has changed much since then, except now everyone talks about the acceptance of unusual families. I am not completely convinced it is true that we live in an accepting society; Britain's problems are far too complex to be a truly accepting nation...

We live on an island and I for one am becoming increasingly worried it may physically sink if we don't stop piling people and buildings on it. But I suppose that's a debate for another day. Being worried about ones island sinking cannot be classed as inappropriate but saying we need to stop people from coming in could be... I think the world is a bit mad at the moment.

My life changed beyond belief when my mum died. I was 13 years old; it was 1982 and I was whisked a hundred miles away to live with my sister, her husband and their four kids. It was heaven. A "normal" family life. No drunken dad and no sharing a house with strangers.

Our houses and lives had always been full of strange, interesting people; I had never minded but this was cool; a new start for us.

As a family we are mad and fantastic we can be quite loud but from that point it was mostly fun.

A solid family unit; strange as it seems this made me realise early on in my life who I was and helped me understand who I was expected to be. It was a good start in life; even though it had been strange and in many ways abusive.

Going from being the baby in one large family to the teenager and big sister in another was strange but I believe it gave me a good start in life.

I wouldn't swap them, well some of them maybe sometimes for a fair price I suppose! Only joking!

Our family parties have been known to put 'Shameless' to shame.

The years I spent in my new family through the eighties saw strong bonds forged with my big sister. She became a mother figure, in a strange she isn't my mum way, and with my nieces in strange little sister ways; especially for my eldest niece Joanne who still struggles to describe Dave as her cousin as she automatically thinks of him as a nephew. She always calls me auntie but the closeness confuses us all; our family has expanded with kids and to be honest we all look at them as a new generation of the family; all equal. The titles don't matter as much as the fact that we are, and always will be "family".

My big sis taught me to value myself and look after myself. Life was hard for her; she was only 24, with four kids of her own under 8 and suddenly my sister and I were dumped on her aged 13 and 15. The social wouldn't give her any money or support to look after her sisters. She was just expected to get on with it. She and her husband often having to work 12 hours a day to support our family; my other sister moved in with her family too, thirteen of us in a three bedroom house for nearly a year; it was cosy.

I can remember Christmas that year. With lots of fun and food but not many presents; it was really good, maybe even one of the best Christmas' ever. Things could only get better; even though it must have been a massive burden for her. She says she wouldn't change a thing other than to have had my mum survive passed her 52nd year; but that we couldn't change, so already my female relatives had taught me at thirteen years old to make the most of life and get on with it.

Eventually, when they housed my sister, Dawn, she took some of the responsibility for stuff. She took Mandy, our other sister, to live with her not faraway from us. As sisters and a growing family we bonded, life was mostly good for us all.

The eighties went from bad to good over a few years. I am certainly very grateful and owe my big sisters a lot; they wouldn't take anything from me but I do owe them. I love them all so much; I repay them all by still letting them look after me! I am still the baby so still get spoilt; it's a hard life being the youngest, but I cope!

My husband's family are very different. Just his parents; one sister and brother. His sister and her partner have two babies now. Not much extended family and not many family friends. It has always seemed quite insular to me. They adored their grandson Dave from the minute he was conceived.

His parents had fallen out with most of their own large families. It seems that there was very little tolerance of the world outside of their house.
Over the last few years we haven't seen them much to be honest.
I don't think it's my business to discuss. This story is about us, not our families. We have been together longer than he was with his family so those years are his business.

He says his parents were quite controlling... At 16 he left home and joined the army; it was 1985.

That bit is only so you can try to understand what made us who we are and when I met Rex he was a happy, arrogant, funny, motivated, young soldier. So his parents couldn't have got too much wrong in bringing him up but they were definitely different to my gang.

Together

I met him in the summer of 1986. He wasn't my usual type; blonde, confident, a little arrogant and cocky but fantastic I thought. We spent all our time together; having a laugh, getting on well then bang his first posting arrived. We were young and in love so by the end of '87 we were married and living in army quarters in Germany; as I mentioned earlier we were both eighteen when we married.

In a lot of ways I refer to it as the 'Soldier Soldier' years. Do you remember the prime time TV 'real life' drama of the eighties that showed a good, funny, light side to being married to a soldier in the eighties? It was very popular.
Robson and Jerome made it even more famous by singing Everly Brother Songs and becoming "pop stars" off the back of it, but in the programme, wives stuck together whilst men went off on exercises, practising to fight wars and playing practical jokes on each other; light, happy days. For the first two years we were married I can remember watching the programme and looking out of the window; seeing 'Donnas' or 'Tuckers' living in our street.

Imagine what Soldier Soldier, a series following squaddies, would be like today. I don't think they see much of the family life so there wouldn't be much light entertainment. Every time I see the news these days my heart breaks for all those families with soldiers serving in the forces. It's so much more intense these days; many blokes don't even get breaks in between tours of war zones from what I hear.

Mr Blair likes to keep them moving that's for sure; so no I don't think it could be classed as light entertainment these days, but soldier soldier was true to life when it was on the telly.

Watching the news most days is like watching a giant game of Risk, the popular world domination game of the eighties. Maybe a good

after diner party game for budding world domination geeks...

Not quite so popular with people when it's a grown man spending our taxes, using our troops, peoples husbands, wives, brothers, sisters, sons and daughters to inflame wars and "peacekeeping" situations that we have no business in - except oil and power.

Soldiers are people, not game tokens to be used to score points with your American friends. How many more will die before they just get them out of places they don't belong. It makes me mad, sorry to rant.

I know for sure that Rex joined up to defend his Queen and his country; being a patriotic sort of bloke. Not to fight politician's dirty wars. Never mind the fact that it is now clearly bringing terrorism to our country...

Anyway where was I, 1987. I had met a lovely, confident young soldier. He loved me, I loved him and life was good. A year later I became pregnant. We had our baby in 1989. It was all good, except living so far away I missed my family. Being used to the usual noise and bustle; now life was very quiet. Sometimes it got me down but having a baby made life better.

He was a happy little baby; always laughing and giggling. I had nearly lost him during the last weeks of my pregnancy so he was extra precious to us both. Rex adored his baby son. It was a very happy time; always out and about, visiting different parts of Germany, seeing friends as we would often get separated from them due to postings.

In the summer of 1990 Rex was posted back to England; at the same time Saddam Hussein invaded Kuwait. Lots of soldiers from our camp went out to the Gulf straight away as we arrived. For us, these were agonising weeks, with him on standby it got to Christmas and still he hadn't gone.

I prayed that he wouldn't have to go but then felt guilty as all around me other wives spent Christmas alone with their kids watching the news each night, as the air strikes got worse and worse. I prayed he wouldn't have to go; we were so young and we had our baby.

By the middle of January 1991 he called me at work to say he was going. I felt sick. He had to leave within the hour! After all this time waiting this was it; I rushed home to see him.

It was hard watching him go; I can only imagine what it was like for him. He was a good soldier; well trained. I knew he was able to do as he was told without thinking about it. He was good at it, not thinking and being a soldier. A clever soldier though, he worked in communications and had a good trade.

It was hard, but then after a few weeks he was shown on the 'News at 10'; driving a land rover off the back of a helicopter in the middle of Kuwait, loads of people saw him and the phone didn't stop ringing for days.
At least I knew he was alive, once they had secured Kuwait the war settled down, the Allied forces were told to leave Saddam for another day. The war was "over"

Eventually he returned; fit and well, looking brown and frazzled but he had a new face; it would later become known as his war face. He frowned with deep lines on his brow and seemed to have aged. He had a birthday whilst he was away but he was still only 22, looking back it was a very harsh way to have to grow up.

The main thing being he was safe. The years ticked by; he went off all over seeing many parts of the world; Hong Kong, Belize, Canada. I stayed home, worked part time and looked after our son. Life was chilled again for a few months at a time in between his tours.

Its 1993; we are on the move again. This time to Northern Ireland; just prior to the ceasefire starting. We had lived with terrorism on a level in Germany; car bombings and shooting, but this was different. Now we were living with it on a daily basis; checking your car, avoiding places that were out of bounds due to terrorism and illegal activities fronted by the IRA. I made some good friends here, it was a very close community forced together by the environment we lived in.

Our son started school and I found myself sat in a primary school in the middle of Northern Ireland praying for peace, alongside people who had been living with terrorism for so many years they had forgotten what peace was. It was sad, scary and anything but peaceful.

We lived with the threat of terror everyday. All that said our 2 years there flew by. I liked it because it was only an hour and half from my family; the closest I'd ever been since leaving home.

Good friends made it bearable; especially my 'bezzy' mate Sharon. We can fill many an hour drinking, telling stories about the mad things we got up to then and in the years since. Like me getting us lost and driving down the Shankill; a definite out of bounds area in Northern Ireland at that time.

We had taken our three kids on a trip to the zoo. It was on all the posters in camp not to go there; one wrong turn out of the zoo was all it took for us to end up in the middle of it - with the kids in the car. All we could do at the time was drive, laugh and try not to look British in our own country. Quite a mad idea when allegedly we were there for the good of the people, according to the politicians of the day.

I told you bits were surreal. It still makes us laugh today, many years on. To be honest, it was very scary at the time and she still insists we wouldn't have got lost if I had listened to her.

My large family back in Yorkshire was growing; many nieces and nephews filled out the family. My eldest niece was to make me a great aunt and I missed them all. I loved my husband, but Army life was hard. The army encouraged the closeness of its soldiers; to ensure a fighting force. This often didn't include or allow for family involvement. The soldiers were always encouraged to meet in the bars and attend functions; breeding many hard-core drinkers.

Back when I had Dave in Germany, many friends of ours at 18 and 19 were in the same hospital as me, drying out. Cool to have so many visitors, but again looking back they were clearly alcoholics. We were all so young; but rules and boundaries were distorted in the army. It was accepted if you drank excessively but not if you had creased trousers or dirty boots; these were kids playing soldiers with no parents to control them. We were all so young, living in Germany with duty-free booze. Yet it was accepted that they drank too much and in some ways expected; the more you could drink the bigger man you were.

It continued wherever we went; different place same sort of activities; I didn't like it. The curse in my family had been alcohol and although I like a drink… Drunken men in those numbers often led to aggression; luckily Rex was never big on drinking. Living as a wife was definitely second-class. Some wives loved it. I had honestly enjoyed parts of it over the years but neither of us were big drinkers. We had our baby; so by this stage I had started to loathe it. I really hated having to give so much of my husband to his job; it didn't leave enough time for our life together. I put up with it but it was getting me down. I had to be with my husband; I loved him and this was his chosen job.

Being posted in Germany again in '95 was buffered by the fact this time we knew a few people; and the fact my good friend Sharon from Ireland had gone to the same place a few weeks before us. This all cushioned the blow a little but I had really wanted to go to the North of England to catch up with my family, but the army said Germany so that was that.

I was getting fed up since the war; he had changed his outlook on life; changed as in he didn't enjoy being away so much anymore either. He liked his home comforts and he wasn't enjoying the regimented way of life the way he used to; the shine goes off after years of being told what to do and when to do it. He loved all the action; every day was different stuff but being a soldier was getting scary. More activity in Bosnia and other places meant blokes were starting to get more frequent active duty. When he had joined up the only wars usually took place in the bar over the last bag of pork scratchings, ten years later the war was with any other country deemed "unstable" by our government, or the American government of course.

I was ready to go to work full time; Dave was six and at school all day. I had a good childminder, Stella she only had one little girl and would have loved a boy to complete her brood. She absolutely adored him and friends would help picking up the slack when it was the holidays.

We started saving; if he was going to leave the army we would need it. He had only signed up for 12 years; this might be the last posting...

He couldn't make up his mind about leaving or extending his time. Then he had a serious skiing accident he bust his knee. He was never a great athlete but he had enjoyed football, rugby and such like. He is a good swimmer and had played water polo. After the accident he took up golf as a gentle, non-contact sport. Most "sport" was attached to social activity in the army so he had had a go at most things to make sure he had a full-ish social life too. He liked one or two pints after these activities as he often chose to stay home when the lads went out on big nights; he valued time as a family.
I even remember marbles and tiddlywinks being played competitively at parties and BBQ's, just to have bets and beer...

The year after his accident was tough; he was off work on crutches, had a couple of operations and was in a lot of pain.
In 1996, just a few days before Christmas, Rex was sent to Bosnia. Things were getting worse over there and quite a few troops from our base in Germany were deployed; for peace keeping duties. He was only away for 6 weeks but something had changed; when he got back again he aged. War and human destruction must have a devastating effect first hand, even watching it on the news is disturbing enough.

It was taking ages for his leg to heal too. We were managing to save a bit of money, but I had some serious health problems, suffering with Gallstones for months and eventually because of incompetent doctors I ended up with an inflamed liver turning me yellow. My friend Sharon was there to crack jokes and keep me smiling all through that dreadful year.
First his leg, Bosnia and then this! Dave was doing ok at school but we were both ill.

When I ended up in hospital having had the offending gall bladder removed, Sharon and our mate Sue turned up to see me. I vaguely remember the visit; they ended up using my Gallstones in a tub as Maracas as they danced around the ward singing. It was very funny and taught me to laugh in extreme circumstances.

A trait not always appropriate, which do you do first when a person falls over; laugh or pick them up? I laugh every time, even if there's blood!

Years later Sharon shocked me when she told me the singing was only to cover how worried she was when she saw me lying in the bed. The operation had gone wrong and I was on morphine, hence the extreme dancing. She is normally impeccably behaved, Ha Ha.

The next year passed quickly working and saving; we both just got on with "it" after being so ill.

We came back to England during the summer of 1997 for a few weeks to visit family and friends. Just like us on the spur of the moment we decided to buy a house. He had decided after months of indecision that he would end his time with the army.

We only came to visit a friend who still lives round the corner from us; we had a nice Chinese, we bought a house and we have ended up staying in the area for the last ten years. Bet you can't guess which friend... Strangely, only a month after moving in I got food poisoning from a dodgy prawn from that takeaway and have never used it since, it is very popular though.

We returned to Germany, he signed the paperwork and was given the news that he would spend his last year in Ireland. This time doing secret stuff... I was moving into our new house back in England just 25 miles away from my family; a big time of change but it all seemed for the best. He wasn't happy since his skiing accident and I certainly wanted to be away from the army. The job in Ireland was the best option for getting home regularly.

So 1997 is quickly turning into a good year; we have Christmas together in our own little house. New years celebrations were to be spent with my family for the first time in an age. We went to stay with my sister; much drink and laughter took over as the New Year began.

As the evening drew to a close, I saw Rex kick off for the first time. He became aggressive and began rambling on about stuff that didn't make sense; I hadn't seen him like this before, he had been in a strange mood all Christmas. We had always had great fun, I can remember the first Christmas we had together, we moved into our army flat on around the 15th of December. We had no creature comforts; all our possessions had been packed in boxes and sent to Germany. But they would take ages to arrive. Rex got on the bus from town to our flat with a real Christmas tree, much to the disgust of the bus driver and the other passengers. We loved Christmas. Normally we had great fun buying far too many prezzies and making it really special for Dave, but this year had been different. We had roots now; our little home together; it felt strange but then change always feels strange.

Rex had always been a happy drunk; a few times he had shouted when things had been kicking off after nights out, normally with other people not us most of us have done that I think. But this New Years Eve was different.

I, my niece Jaimie and her fella Ben ended up chasing Rex around the streets for hours; he was really upset and threatening to hang himself. It had started over nothing, he just got upset and started talking about stuff that had happened in the Army and ran off. Luckily he had just got his first mobile phone so as we looked for him we could speak to him on the phone, it was very strange.

I don't know were it came from but the next day he only remembered bits and pieces.

1998 started strangely but he was flying back out to Ireland on New Years day, so no point in going on about it I thought. It had probably been a bad mix of cheap drink; far too much of it and after fourteen years his time in the Army was ending. It was a big decision to make; he was bound to be stressed.

For the next year we lived apart. I worked a lot of hours cleaning, setting up my own little business to fit in with school hours and sometimes working nights as a support worker to boost our funds. We had borrowed money to buy the house and I wanted to change a lot of the decoration. Rex came home every 6 weeks to visit.

These were good times; he was drinking a lot when he came home but he said it was his holiday so why not. I knew he was doing a stressful job out there and that he had been making lots of good mates in the bar. They were a very close troop, working together and socialising together too. They were based in a compound some where all there was in the compound was a bar and a barrack block, other than the office or work space.

I was busy working and getting back in touch with family life. I had missed them all for a lot of years and I had a lot of making up to do.

His time in the army was coming to an end. I thought he was just preparing for the shock of living in the real world. He was drinking more than he ever had but then we had both been institutionalised by the time we had spent in the Army environment. We both would need to adjust over the coming months. I was just really enjoying life back with my family not too far away, my good friend just around the corner; life was good.

The best thing about spending just over ten years buffered by the army was we had completely missed a decade in this country. One when it seems the country had been hit by many things including the recession and countless repossession of family homes, loss of industry the bit we had left and many redundancies.

The country somehow felt flatter than before.

I will speculate on why I think it might be because it's my book; perhaps the steady in-flux of asylum seekers in this country, could it be our government getting involved with more peacekeeping duties for our soldiers? Maybe more "displaced people"; if that's the right term have been turning up on our doorsteps. There are definitely more drug and alcohol issues in society. This could be linked to the nations "poor mental health". We read daily about the affects of "broken family units"; hoodies and chavs taking over the streets, the media labelling youths has caused problems with them being demonised as a generation. I really don't know what it is but whatever it was it didn't quite feel like the country we had left in 1987 and we'd only been away for ten years.

There certainly seemed less social divide than before we left but there were also less social responsibilities. Communities dwindling as families were separated by lack of local employment and housing, and rising house prices. The workforce had become transient now; it seems better-paid jobs influenced where people lived rather than family roots.
I knew most people in our neighbourhood when I was growing up but now it seemed like every man, woman and child for themselves.

The army had kept us away from reality in many ways, but I was sure we wouldn't miss it that much; life is after all what you make it.

Freedom

He finished in the army just after the Christmas of 1999. It was a good feeling us three back together. He got a job and we went on a big family holiday with Fred and his lot. The Greek bug was planted; we had been the year before with Jaimie and her Dad Jim; the break did us good. We had two weeks in the sun and then got on with the business of settling down into our new life together.

It soon became apparent that he didn't think his new job paid well enough; he was working on a millennium project for a utility company. We had both been happy and relieved that he had a job to go to after all those years in the Army. One of his big worries had been getting a job.
He often made me laugh with stories about people he met in the day, especially when a woman of a certain age in her bathrobe tried to talk him into giving her free utilities in exchange for … He didn't think that the job paid well enough to be scared like that on a daily basis, so he began looking for something else.

He landed a job with a large communication company engineering. The hours were good as was the money; it really was a spot on job. The only downside was that he was working outside in all weathers. He hated that bit of his job with a passion in the winter months. Looking back, winters had become a bad time for us both, the last two anyway. It just seemed doom and gloom had taken over the Christmas spirit. Every time he had been away on active duty it had been within December or January. Whilst he was in the army, we had approximately six consecutive years where he missed my birthday at the beginning of March.

Over the next few years I worked and went to college part time. I had found that I loved working with people with mental health problems. Working with people means life is never dull and working with mad people means it's never dull or boring. Everyday was a different challenge. I loved it. I was going to train to be a nurse after years of being a wife in the army environment meaning that I had always done little jobs, stuff to fit in with the army. I was doing something for myself; remember for long spells I would be left as a single parent so Dave had always had to come first for me.

I had worked in the Army years as I call them doing loads of different stuff; a spell doing voluntary work, setting up support services for Gulf War wives back in 1991. I had loved being involved in that. During that time I also did a spell as a bingo caller! I had also worked full time as an accounts manager in Germany so I knew I could do more than I had been doing. I concentrated on getting to uni so I could make a semi decent living as a nurse. Some weeks with work and college it could be seventy hours but I just wanted to get on. Hard work is the only thing that pays consistently. I believe it doesn't matter what you do as long as you work hard at it, it will pay eventually.

I decided at 30 it was time for me to be me. I started to realise how I had been made to change who I was by my forced environment; army life was quite controlling. The army controlled everything even your social life was dictated by your husband's rank and wives invitations. They picked where we lived, who we were friends with but most annoyingly they picked how much time was spent together as a family.

Still, no regrets for either of us; he did miss some bits of it though.

By now I was working in a fantastic unit for people with brain injuries doing rehab and behaviour therapy. I passed my access course and was offered a place at university to study mental health nursing. Studying mental health also meant I could understand why I felt like I did sometimes and how to control my fed up times. I turned all my energy into trying to make positive changes for me, so my family could change shape too.
Rex was always talking about university. I thought if only I could make more money he would be able to work part time and go to university too.

With the bursary, and continuing to work part time I would be better off financially. I would be able to earn more and ease the obvious burden he was feeling now. We had every day stresses like mortgage and bills to deal with. I looked after most of it but it seemed to be getting him down. We were doing ok but that's not how he felt.

By the year 2000 he had started to show signs of depression and anxiety. He didn't drink often but when he did he couldn't stop; he would get very drunk and occasionally he got aggressive. By this stage he had started to realise there was something wrong. He still didn't want to admit he had a mental health problem though but he had never behaved or felt like this before.

He continued to work full time but his mood and self-confidence were all over the place. Many of our friends and family had seen him drunk and aggressive by now. He did try not having a drink sometimes when we went out; he knew he really couldn't control it once he started. At that stage he found it hard to go into a pub and not drink; that made having a social life hard. We had built a good solid group of friends at long last after years of moving on and being forced into friendships because of the army environment, now it was going down the pan because he was ill.

It was difficult managing to see people without some sort of problem. He would arrange things and then not go; letting me make excuses. Life was becoming unbearable. He was becoming more and more unwell and all I could do was watch his moods spiral downwards whilst he just blamed me for most of his problems; wanting to blame anything other than admit the truth that he was ill.

I had started a new job instead of going to university. He still kept saying he wanted to go to college so I hunted around and found a well-paid job, so that he would have more choices; he still didn't go to college.
I left a job I had loved doing working with fantastic people and given up a place in university but he still didn't get of his bum to change

63

things. Looking back, it is obvious why he couldn't; his mental health was deteriorating fast. At the time it caused argument after argument in my house.

Rex had changed into some sort of anxious, aggressive, unreasonable, depressed, sometimes-manic person. It seemed like he did want to do stuff like change his job, his life, but something was stopping him and he blamed me. I thought he was ill, as did our GP and others, but he still didn't believe he was. Our GP thought he was depressed because of leaving the Army but that was only a bit of the truth.

Since leaving the army he had developed a habit of screaming and shouting at me for hours. This was because he was angry, but by the time he'd finished shouting it would be hard to remember what it was he was angry about in the first place. He was just angry but I was getting tired of it all. At other times he'd be depressed and crying for days.

It became a way of life. Sometimes he'd start shouting over not ringing, not parking straight, in fact I think at some stages it has been just for breathing. It was clear there was something wrong with him; nothing could make him happy anymore. It had become impossible to live with him.

Dave understood clearly that his Dad was suffering from some sort of illness; we all could, but it was hard to pin down what it was. It seemed to be many illnesses rolled into one, but it did make life difficult for us all.

He went to see the GP a few times when there had been serious incidents. He has been aggressive with me a couple of times; some of the stuff he has done has been outrageous. Sometimes me challenging over things has wound him up to the point of aggression and just to be fair I must say I didn't stand around doing nothing; I hit him back every time.

I don't want anyone reporting this as domestic violence. In its truest form domestic violence is an unforgivable, despicable crime; a person being so scared for their own safety and/or sanity that they cannot get out of a situation is not the environment I am trying to describe.

I had watched other woman around me take abuse from men in the past. I had never had to; he had never been aggressive to me before he was mad. Part of the reason I stuck by him was because I understood what was happening when he started on me. I had been trained to watch behaviours and look after people in crisis, but I wasn't going to take it from him just because he was mad.
No one has a right to hit another person, but self-defence is ok in my book and this is my book.
By whacking him back I made sure it didn't happen too often but it did happen a few times, always when he was drunk.

Anyway, the upshot is his post-traumatic stress had gone untreated for several years. He had been given Prozac for his depression but it didn't work. They tried this a few times. I even went with him to see our GP to try and explain the mood swings and things. I told our doctor about the mania. After many months he was referred to the psychology department at our local hospital.

I had told him to be honest with the doctor. He told him what had happened since he left the army; the fact he was getting absolutely wasted on drink and getting aggressive towards me, and the problems that was causing. He also mentioned he had smoked a little bit of weed within a twenty minute session; the consultant decided that the weed must surely be the problem. The doctor told him to stop smoking pot and sent him for counselling; thirty minutes later that was his diagnosis done.

Rex came away worse than he went in; convinced he was a junkie. Neither of us had felt that the pot was an issue before he went in, maybe the drink had been out of control and very dangerous. Smoking the evil weed a couple of times in the last couple of months had made him giggle and chill out. We couldn't understand why the doctor had said this; the illness had been about for maybe four years or more; the pot a few times in the last four or five months; a big issue to the doctor because it's illegal. He never mentioned the drink problem; only the truth about his behaviour whilst drunk.

On the rare occasion that he could get a joint he'd happily spend a Friday night sat with friends chilling out. No shouting, no cursing, just Rex. Now the doctor had said this must stop. That meant he would go back to the drink...

He hadn't said don't drink, so the weed stopped and the drink started again; setting us off back down the road of drink fuelled madness. Thank you very much, Dr Nopal. Yes the very same consultant who years later wrongly filled in the paperwork for the DVLA.

Rex did try to cope but he now felt like he'd been labelled a "junkie". He met one of the assistant psychologists he had had a few sessions with; a Guy called Luke. He saw him a few times; Luke suggested that Rex may have been suffering from Post Traumatic Stress; he seemed to have had a lot of the symptoms...
He missed two sessions as he didn't want to let them know at work about his appointments. Not wanting to have to explain what the appointments were for, and being one of the worst liars I have ever met, telling lots of fibs were out of the question. Hospital policy is that after two missed appointments he would be taken off the list; he tried to rearrange a few times before he gave up. Then it was back to the GP, he has to re-refer you and then you have to wait again.

As I sit here today I can swear that if the drink had continued, I'd probably have been seriously hurt. I can also say that his illness had started long before he had his first joint; that just offered an alternative to drink. He is a grown-up; smoking a bit of weed isn't the end of anyone's world. He was coping with a full-time job, his mental health was poor and he'd smoked a couple of joints - the doctor had told Rex it had ruined his life. No interest at all in sorting out the real problems. Thank god for the NHS!

Now he was really struggling; he knew the drink had to be seriously controlled. He'd seen the effect on me; most times when he started drinking I would burst into tears.

I knew what the climax of most of his drinking sessions would be and that did deter him a little. The doctor said no weed; Rex knew he couldn't drink, but there was no treatment on offer either.

Looking back he did control the drinking extremely well; by cutting us off from the world. But that only happened because of the circumstances. I allowed it to happen; I wanted to protect him. Remember we had been together for along time; he deserved my loyalty and support. It certainly wasn't his fault; he'd become ill. He just didn't understand it well enough to ask for the right treatment.

So we carried on for the next year; me trying to keep him afloat and him trying to keep himself together.

Despite living with his mental health problem and having a hard time most days at home; at work I was doing well. My new job was a challenge; a whole new direction in supported housing and community support services; yet I had ended up getting two promotions and decent pay rises to match, all within eighteen months.

After the second promotion I had worked extremely hard for, Rex didn't speak to me for 3 days. He said I was showing off his low self-esteem. Confidence at rock bottom, I could understand his response, but it was an exciting time for me; I tried not to let his stuff drag me down.

It was Christmas again and he was back struggling to work through the winter months. It had become a bad time of year since he had left the army; up until then we had enjoyed very special Christmas'. When Dave was small we always made a big fuss; but not anymore. It is Dave's 15th Christmas, Rex had been off work sick several times in recent months; I had encouraged him to tell his boss about his illness.

Eventually he did. Not having managers that know how to support staff meant he was sent straight to an Occupational Health Company.

At work we also use one, to help people understand what the problem is, what's causing them and how it affects themselves and their jobs. The nurse there wasn't very helpful; she said he had a chip on his shoulder and that he should leave his job if it made him so unhappy. The nurse was obviously working on the information sent to her by her manager.

She even went on to say that most people would kill for a job with a big firm like the one he worked for and he should stop moaning. I'd love to meet this nurse; the one that pushed him over the edge. She may be a very good nurse but using these companies which can be used by employers to try and manage people, by getting medical opinions based on twenty minute consultations and using reports based on those twenty minutes to try and "manage" them. The responsibility for employee welfare is put in the hands of strangers who don't know the employee; instead of the liability lying with the people that manage them. It's a management cop out. Occasionally they can be extremely helpful if employees need physical assessments, or have long term health problems. But he had just approached his manager for help, a bit of understanding. He was really ill; begging for help and all she told him was that he was just a moaning git and to get a life; it really wasn't helpful.

It wasn't his job that was the major problem, it was his illness. Although a lot of the manager's decisions; employing his relatives and stuff were not good practice. I am sure he could have tried a little harder to help Rex out; he was a good worker. Most of the blokes didn't mind working with him as they knew he got the job done. I'm not sure if they have policies about equality and stuff but you would think quite possibly the biggest communication company in this country would have. The way they treat their engineers is crap; they did nothing to help.

Mental illness is an invisible disability and this large company discriminated against him. In fact his local line manager even poked fun at him, shouting over the yard one day about "being miserable because of his depression"; making sure all of Rex's workmates heard what he said. Rex was devastated. Some people he worked with knew by that stage but they had kept stuff to themselves; he had made a few good mates at work.

A thing he used to say to me all the time back then was "no one understands me" and it is only in the last months that I have truly understood what he meant. Since he left the army no one has understood him.

The blokes he worked with now had been car audio fitters, factory workers, green grocers, electricians; he'd been a soldier and that is very very different. Going to war with your mates isn't like a lad's holiday in Benidorm. How could anyone understand it unless they'd been there?

I think the manager thought it was a joke. I wanted to go up to the yard and smash his face in but my job is dependant on a police check; it helps to control such urges but it doesn't stop you from having them.

His mood had been low right through to March for the last few years. I had lost my dad a few years previously in February so it wasn't a good time for me either. Winter was bleak at best.

Christmas and New Year were over. The usual round of trying to keep him happy was a battle. He was so down and stressed I just couldn't help him, the verbal abuse just continued.

By this time my concerns were starting to change; Dave was getting older and he saw more of the trouble between me and his dad. He felt protective of me and I was becoming worried that a situation might arise whilst I wasn't home to calm it down. Our son is patient, kind and eternally fair but my husband's behaviour was becoming outrageous. Often Rex could start on him for no reason. Dave being his mother's son had started standing up to his dad.

I loved working hard to help my staff teams to help others. Some knew bits about stuff at home and were really supportive. I felt lucky at that time. We had enough money, a nice house, both had a car but his illness had taken over 90 percent of all of our lives and that couldn't continue.

I sought advice about divorcing him; I wasn't giving up easy. The last few years had seen my big soft husband, a trained killer and confirmed good husband had turned into a manic mess. But still he wouldn't tell the GP enough to get a referral to go back to the psychology department. Dr Nopal had made him believe he was a druggie because of a few spliffs and he didn't want to go back there. Occasionally, we still got it to keep the drink at bay, it chilled him out but what the consultant said stuck in his mind.

I wasn't running away but I had our son to think about. In his less frequent calm periods Rex agreed that he didn't want our family to continue this way. I had tried everything I could to make it work for us all; to make him happy. Even he started to realise I couldn't do that he would have to do that for himself.
He asked me not to divorce him; he said he was going to sort himself out. I was at the end of my tether and he was past himself, neither of us knew what to do next.

He handed in his notice at work; he couldn't face going in. He knew that people had heard what his manager had said, and it had taken his last bit of confidence. My brother's stuff was just starting up in Greece and he was going to go over there for a few months to help. He planned to take a working type of a holiday break.
He had been working non-stop for twenty years and for many of the, in probably one of the most stressful jobs on the planet. A long break was the least he deserved.

By March 2005 he was off on his travels. I was left holding the fort, I bought my car from him, he had given me this as a gift the year before but now he wanted the money for it. That was cool except he ripped me off... I paid what he had on the loan not what it was worth.

He spent the next six months back and forth between here and there and we went over for a few sunny breaks too. It was cool he was chilling out in some ways but obviously walking out of a well paid job was hard.

In some ways he was coping well but in others it was clear that he was struggling; emotionally he seemed exhausted.

His mental health was up and down but he was coping. At least he was working a bit. By October he was back full time living in our house, his mood was very flat.

He was trying not to shout. I think he realised he had no control over me at last. We have been part of a good couple for a long time but we were still individuals he wasn't contributing financially. I was paying for and providing everything; so he thought he should behave, he was on thin ice.

I think that became part of the problem then, he measured how manly he was by what he contributed, he has always provided well up to this point and I could tell he was uncomfortable with the situation.

I love him very much. We had been together 19 years by this stage. He decided to go and make some money taxi driving. I wanted him to sort himself out, so when he didn't have a car to taxi with, it was no problem he just took mine back and registered it back in his name; even though I'd paid for it… It was theft before my very eyes.

I let him do it so I take some blame. He was trying to keep it together so that he could hang around for Christmas. He has no one except for us, me and Dave so how could I do anything else than let him get away with it; it was really starting to get on my nerves.

I was left again with no car, no money and a job that took me on a 300 mile round journey each week. Even work started going wrong at that point. A management restructure was taking place and we were competing for jobs. I daren't even get much of a loan for a car; I didn't know if I had a job.

I knew that I had worked hard for them and felt quite secure in my post, but who knows. I had to take out a small loan and became the owner of an old Suzuki.

I love him, I really need to consider something new but I can't face getting rid of him, I have had him two years next month.

I did have a massive mortgage, a kid in his final year at school, and my mad old soldier. Life was truly crap and very stressful. I was going through a recruitment process; he was working nights taxiing and getting a bit verbal again; getting stressed because he didn't want to be taxiing. I am surprised I kept going but you have to, if you give up nothing goes away so you may as well keep trying. He was quite ill again up and down but winter was looming I wasn't too surprised by it really.

Early November I got a call from a senior manager in my area saying that I had failed the recruitment process and was going to be made redundant.

I almost laughed, I knew there must be a mistake yet the impact on Rex was amazing. I was very angry but I wasn't worried about losing my job; I just knew there had been a mistake.

I just had to be cool about it. I had applied for another job and if I started arguing at work at this stage I might have lost out on other opportunities.

Sometimes, and this was one of them, I amaze myself how I keep cool. I am not even sure how I do it but self control in some areas is easy; controlling behaviour is much easier than controlling a diet that's for sure.

Rex was very down, it must have been hard. He did worry about me carrying the burden. We had more or less the same lifestyle as last year but with 25 grand less in the bank. I know he is a good man and has always been a good provider; Dave and I have never gone without any thing as my sister is always reminding me. He had always worked and wanted to provide well but he was only bringing in enough to cover his own outgoings and food shopping each week.

He was working as much as his illness allowed but not a lot, it really was any excuse not to go in.

Anyway the money was a drop in the ocean really by this stage, over spending and extravagant gifts had all been on credit over the last few years. We had earned plenty but spent more like most people. The only thing was most of it now sat on a massive mortgage around my neck.

I'd just get up in a morning and go to work but he went off the rails for weeks, worrying about how I'd pay the mortgage if I really was redundant.

By December I sat down with my regional director; let's call him Dirk for fun.

He is a lovely man, very fair and open. I asked him to explain how I had been made redundant. I still couldn't understand what had gone wrong; all the evidence in my portfolio was of managing very good services. I knew that a mistake had occurred and asked for this to be investigated.

I was very stressed and angry and I am sure I swore several times during my meeting with him.

I had worked very hard and felt very let down, He listened and made lots of tea and promised to look into it.

A few days later the mistake was confirmed but I think the damage was already done. They reinstated me and Dirk apologised. As I said to him direct at that stage it wasn't his mistake but he did apologise many times. I lost a lot of faith in the organisation.

Life at home bobbed along; he knew I could pay the mortgage and that was all that mattered. He seemed less stressed now he knew the finances were covered again.

Just before Christmas 2005, I went out to a Christmas lunch. Champagne cocktails at lunch time, boy was I pissed. Some nice French food; if there is such a thing. My friend Ricardo assured me there was but I was far too drunk to notice. Along with Bruce, Cilla and some others, our lunch turned into many hours drinking; just a few work friends having far too much wine, the company was very funny...Bruce was hilarious; he has this high pitched girly giggle which had been making me laugh for months at work. I am sure he will kill me for putting that into print but it's true.

I behaved outrageously and had one of the best nights out ever. I had forgotten what it was like to enjoy other peoples company and be myself.
It made me extremely sad as I remembered how much fun our life used to be, once I'd sobered up.

I hadn't been out by myself for ages and most nights out in recent years together had seen me trying to control Rex and his problem. As soon as he had too much to drink it would be a battle.
If I went out by myself he worried I wouldn't come back often texting and ringing until I gave in and came home.

This was an interesting, carefree night; the likes of which I hadn't had for ages. The next day I woke up thinking about changing things positively for us all; I was sick of being sad and unhappy.

Life is for living and I realised how much it was passing me by very quickly these days. I didn't make it to work which was a shame, I think it would have been good to laugh off some of my drunken outrageous behaviour from the night before. I wasn't worried, all sorts happen at Christmas parties and it wasn't like I had sex on the photocopier or anything.
It was also my closest work mates so no one would be talking about it in work anyway. I just lay on the sofa and died with a hangover, a glass of orange juice, and a big smile on my face. Something had changed; even though my head was pounding like mad and I was feeling a sicker than a sick feeling; I felt optimistic again. It was a welcome feeling.

It made me realise what I was missing out on. Not that I want to leave Rex but that I wanted my life back. He seemed to have taken it or maybe I had given it but it was definitely gone and I blamed his illness for ages. Now I realised part of the problem was that I had given my life up to look after and protect him.

In honesty there was very little life left in me anymore and even less in our relationship. It had taken a real battering over the last years and it was definitely time to take stock.

He or his illness had come to control all of our lives, all except for when I was at work and Dave was at school; even then some days he could ring me about twenty times, manic about stuff and always anxious about when I would come back. He was totally dependant on me.

I had been trying to stop it, he had never been a clingy husband but now it was firmly there, even he noticed how bad it was getting.

He had no one else to turn to and he thought seriously about going back out to Greece, he had made many friends there.

There was no one else to blame for anything anymore he had got himself into a mess over the last few years. The loss of the controlled environment that institutionalised him in the army had left an angry, frustrated, stressed, anxious mess. It made me very sad.

I was mad thinking I could keep it all together, but he had not spoken to his own family very much over the years. Every time I tried to pull away, he upped the stakes to make me stay. He was scared of being on his own but he knew we couldn't stay in this situation forever.

With a New Year starting I was trying to encourage him to make positive changes. He had been to Greece with my brother last year and made some good friends, he could go back over. He suggested we could look at selling the house then I could pay him his half and he could start a small business for himself. It sounded to me like I was about to lose out financially again. I didn't care about money, it comes and it goes, so what's the point in worrying.

The idea grew and I went to get mortgage advice. He was putting pressure on me demanding that I sort it out quickly. He thinks you can buy and sell houses in a week, but then he has never done anything like deal with bills, money, chores, daily stuff. You know real life stuff.

Eventually it was all sorted. I bought our house off him at a once only price. I had learnt my lesson with the car the year previously and I wasn't being ripped off again.
I was skint but still trying anything I could to help him out. After this he couldn't take anymore emotionally or financially, he agrees and the deal is done.

I know I'm out of pocket again but this time I tell him to sling his hook when he offers me a bargain car, registered as a taxi. I was starting to get angry, really angry. For the first time he did realise what he was doing on some level and I had to stop before it ruined me completely.

Although his mental health was fairly good he still had some days when he would be very manic. One day in February as I walked down to the sandwich shop with my work mate Bruce, we had been in a meeting and had a short break so we were rushing. As we rushed and chatted I picked up a message from my phone; there had been several missed calls from Rex and eventually he left a message saying he was going to burn the house down with me in it. I tried to keep up the conversation with Bruce and had to sit through the afternoon session of the meeting. This was one of the days when the girly giggle laugh kept me sane, it's for days like this that the outrageous laughter of friends comes in handy. I knew Rex was just trying to intimidate me as he thought I was ignoring him but I was so tired of it; I wanted to lie on the floor and cry. This sort of threatening had started a year ago. Thankfully, it didn't happen that often. I was shocked as he had seemed more settled and ready to go. Part of me was extremely relieved that this was going to end soon. As much as I understood his illness; I'd had enough. I had grown tired of having to put up with this madness that had become our lives. I had to work hard and having to worry about my house burning down in the middle of a disciplinary hearing at work was just too much. I smiled again, knowing that at last I was taking some control.

It was hard getting by, in some ways I felt like I wanted to be rid of him, and other ways I wanted to look after him. I couldn't do it anymore, and he didn't want me to look after him either. The more ill he became the more dependant he became. We both knew it wasn't healthy, that was why he had been away the year before.

I'm a believer

February became very cold and icy towards the end of the month; it was snowing and foggy. As I left work one night some people from our regional office had arranged to go and see a clairvoyant by the name of Terry. They had invited me along knowing I had an interest in Spiritualism and such stuff. I ummed and arghed about going, the weather was really bad. I travel an hour to work and this would take me another 3 junctions down the M1 away from home. The car seemed to have a mind of his own as we got to the motorway; we turned left instead of right and set of towards the house. I have always been a believer and apparently, this guy was amazing.

I was there with several people from work. We had booked it through Nicky's mum. We had made a pact to say nothing, give nothing away. We also tested the sound proofing in the kitchen; you certainly couldn't hear through the walls.

Terry walked through the lounge into the kitchen; smiling at us as he went through, but no introductions. Our friend Alison went in first; she came out looking pale - but smiling. I was next. As I walked in the atmosphere was strange; even though it was just Nicky's mums kitchen it hadn't felt like this before; we had messed about listening to each other before he arrived.

I swear on my life my dad was in the room. As I walked in Terry called me by my name; I sat down and it began. He talked about so many things; he said my dad had been waiting for me to turn up, the things he told me wasn't stuff even known to my work colleagues and this man had never met me before. He talked and talked for twenty minutes, my mind was racing. I was glad it was being taped. I couldn't take it all in; once again I was speechless.

Over the years I had seen many psychics. My mum who had been dead for many years had never contacted me before now; she was hanging out in the shadows according to Terry. The details were truly unbelievable; he said she didn't really want to talk to me and that we'd make it up when we met again. It all made perfect sense and since he told me this stuff I have been able to make my peace with her in my head. I was only thirteen when she died; it has taken many years for me to find answers that allow me to think of her as my mum; not an evil witch who left me too early.

I did once get a strange message that I thought was from her. It was at one of those large "spiritual" gatherings with a quite famous clairvoyant called Stephen. One of his spirit guides was Marti Caine; a singer from the seventies and acquaintance of my mother. At the end of his show, my friend Liz and I went halves on his book; it was only a fiver. We'd only read it once; I gave her my half of the money and she went to queue up to by it.

I went to the loo. Liz came back looking puzzled; she explained that he had wrote a strange message in the front about being a wonderful daughter with love from a wonderful mother.
Liz was concerned; her mum is alive and well and living round the corner. We talked about it as we walked home and the only thing we could think of was the connection between my mum and Marti Caine.

Other than that little "message" I have had nothing, and like I said I have been to see a few psychics over the years.
Now it seemed that my Dad had come to me at one of my lowest points. Again looking back over the past few years I realised this was my first visit to see a clairvoyant since my dad had died, so maybe it was him that wanted to talk to me and she was just there hanging about with him.

Lots of things started to make sense; he said he only saw positive change at this stage. He told me about buying my house and everything that had been going on, without me giving anything away. I couldn't speak to give anything away; I was truly amazed.
The 'for sale' sign had just gone up that day.

The only problem was, as I drove home I tried to push the tape into my car stereo. I ended up weaving all over the road as I couldn't get it in. It took about twenty miles of swerving before I realised I only have a CD player in the car.

I think I was in shock and I couldn't quite believe what I had just heard. To be honest it scared me a little; it's like believing in ghosts and walking into a room to find a big white spook in front of you; or maybe finding God at your door if you are a Christian.

I listened to the tape when I got in; Rex sat with his mouth open - also unable to believe what he was hearing. The most shocking bits; when he spoke about my husband having problems. He said something like 'you can take the man out of the army but you can't take the army out of the man'. He also said that there had been times when he should leave his anger outside the home. It was so accurate it was unbelievable.

Later, my sisters listened to the tape and couldn't believe it either; again I felt positive. I had always been my dad's favourite and was pleased to feel that someone was on my side looking out for me at last.

Things started looking up. I am not sure why it made me feel good but it did. I suppose getting proof of something I believed in for all those years certainly helped for some strange reason.

Rex was looking forward to getting away again. Things weren't too bad to be honest and by this time it was only a few weeks and he'd be off again. I had done everything I could to keep him afloat but it was time for him to stand on his own two feet. I think he had been spoilt, pampered and maybe a little too well looked after for far too long. I think I have been quite weak at times but then, I took my vows seriously.

Better or worse, sickness and health. It wasn't his fault he'd developed this problem. Looking after him the last few years had been hard work but again the overriding thought is that you can't just drop people because they are not well.

He was looking forward to Greece but he wasn't working at all now. He was stressing about being skint; he was waiting for his money from the sale of the house. I had just turned 37 which made me just a few weeks older than he was. He was to celebrate his birthday just after he left.

A few weeks later, after recommending Terry to everyone I knew, I saw him again; this time at a different friend's house. My niece was there but he didn't pick up a connection. Maybe he was a fraud…

He gave even more detail; my mum's name was uttered and assurance that things should keep changing. It was a good reading, but I think I was a little disappointed. I think the biggest shock the time before was his accuracy; this time I expected a lot. The only thing that freaked me out this time was when he said that "he just hoped everything would stay ok". What did that mean? If I believed the good bits, I had to take heed of the bad bits.

I pushed it to the back of my mind; got on with helping Rex to get ready for his move. Dave was trying to concentrate on his exams that were just ready to start. His intense study period was just days away; no time for worrying. I felt that everything was going to be ok - what did the clairvoyant know?

He had been good; mostly positive, and I managed to push the negative thoughts to the back of my mind. I am a firm believer in just getting on with things. Most things that go wrong are things you can't change, so no point stressing; what will be will be.

Time was passing quickly and eventually the day came. Dave and I drove Rex to the airport. We wanted to go in and keep him company but he said no. I suppose that was his old army training kicking in; telling him to walk away and go.

I started to cry as he walked away; I knew that this had gone too far. It's hard work looking after someone when they refuse to admit they are ill. He was trained not to think too much for fourteen years; I believe he had even managed to use his training to block out how ill he'd become.

He knew deep inside that running away wasn't the answer but he didn't know what to do, and I was lost. I had worked with people with mental health problems for years but this illness was different. He had been treated for depression but it hadn't helped. It is so many different things on different days; manic depression, anxiety, stress to name but a few but he was still my husband underneath all that, and he was ill.

Anyway, we were optimistic that this plan would work this time. We all wanted desperately to be happy. Dave and I just wanted him to be the happy person we loved so much but didn't see that often; the messed up Rex was here most of the time now.
Rex wanted to make a new start so he could start getting better in himself, or so he said. He was trying his hardest to control his symptoms but some days it was clear it was too much for us to deal with. He had to make his own choices about what he had to do.

A couple of days later I was in a meeting with my manager. I asked for some support at work; I had never asked for anything and I had worked hard for them for some years. I wanted to extend my probationary period before making a commitment to the new job I had got during the restructure. I was travelling huge distances every day to my new job and not enjoying it at all; I just wanted some time, some breathing space.

That week I had dropped Rex of at the airport on a Tuesday; spent all day Wednesday in a disciplinary hearing that had been dragging on for a year.
On Thursday the meeting took place and for the first time ever since joining the organisation I left the building in tears; my brain was boggled.
Unfortunately I was told that if I didn't sign up to the job now then I would be given my 4 weeks notice. This seemed to push me over the

edge; other people were getting extensions for lots of different reasons; it wouldn't have been hard to give me a few more weeks. But it wasn't on offer for me; I thought my manager wanted rid of me. Why would she refuse it? I couldn't understand, she knew what had been happening at home.

The organisation I work for isn't always fair to its employees. They just pay lip service to supporting staff; sometimes I am sure it is like most other places but for me this took the biscuit.
But at least at home I had peace and quiet at last. I was very worried about Dave and his GCSE's but there was nothing I could do at this stage; except support him in anyway possible. We are very close and have always had to make time for each other away from Rex; to some extent Rex had even been jealous of our relationship. As he had pushed us both away, we just got closer. Not on purpose, it just happened. That made the jealousy even worse.

Work stuff was getting a bit too much; I'd often get palpitations bought on by stress. These were getting worse. You know what it's like once you have had a crisis in your life; as soon as it's over you get the flu or a bug of some description. I felt lousy; a reaction to everything I think. The day I was threatened with my notice triggered a really sick feeling. I sobbed all the way home; now I had an extra worry; a hundred grand mortgage and the threat of losing my job again. I couldn't take much more so I saw my GP. He advised me to take some time off. The last six months had been hell triggered by my redundancy process at work. The doctor thought I was stressed and exhausted; I must admit I did feel rotten.

It was as though while Rex had been about I had kept going to work; it was easier than staying home. I had only taken a week off work sick in the last three and a half years; hardly a bad sick record. So when the doctor suggested a week off I knew I needed it and would take it. I was committed to my job one hundred and twenty percent but this lot of poor management was too much, so I went home and called my boss.

I know, looking back, everyone in our place was more than stressed at that time and things happened that shouldn't have, but it triggered my longest stay off work ever...

It was a sunny Thursday in April; Rex had been gone for a couple of weeks and I looked forward to some rest, and time to think about me for a change. I had a little bit of money left from my mortgage, I'd amuse myself for a week chilling out and getting a new fence and fire. Rex didn't like having workmen round; he could become quite paranoid, so I could at least sort some stuff out at home. That would make me feel much better.

That way, work would get back into perspective. It really is no problem; it's just a job. Life is all about balance and work hadn't bothered me; whilst I had bigger problems at home it seemed now they were gone; work had taken over. I knew I just needed to get the balance back on track.

It was then the calls started. The weekend after Easter, Rex had only been gone three weeks. Friends kept saying he was behaving strangely; delusional. I spoke to my brother; we both thought he had probably been drinking.
It transpired over the next twenty-four hours that he wasn't drinking; he'd had some sort of breakdown…

I had been trying to contact him for three days. Never in all the years, have we gone that long without talking without good reason, like a war or a jungle stopping us.

My brother flew directly over and brought him home. God bless Easy Jet, he was completely bonkers. Like I have said, he was making some sense to those that know him. I can imagine travelling with him was very difficult; he was severely dehydrated and kept being sick. He said he kept wandering off; you needed eyes up your bum to watch him.

He refused to get on the flight until he had bought me a present. A four hundred quid spend later and my brother had to drag him into the departure lounge.

My brother said the cabin staff on the flight from Athens was fantastic; doing everything they could to help.

He had been attacked by a gang and run over by a motorbike for trying to help a tramp. By the time the tramp got help to where the attack had taken place it was too late, Rex had wandered off; lost in the blistering heat. They looked around but couldn't find him. They thought he would turn up at the bars or apartments. He did turn up; but not until many hours later; burnt from the sun, terrible blisters on his feet and legs, and showing serious signs of sunstroke.

As I spoke to my brother it became clear Rex was in a bad way; he knew who he was and why he was there. He desperately wanted to come home to me and Dave.

My brother was exhausted as he walked through the gate. Rex was quite hyper. I met them at the airport; we got in the car and headed for home, dropping my brother off on the way.
Rex was crying and talking at a rapid pace, but as we drove he was slowing down; I could see him visibly relaxing. It would be cool; the thought ran through my mind again; relief I think that he had to now get help for his mental health problems; he could no longer deny how bad he was to me, others or himself.

I always remember what song is playing when something is happening in my life; tonight it was Cold Play's Fix U on the radio....

Being in communications, and thinking he was a secret agent who had to come back from Greece to look after his family; he began to play with the radio stations. I swear all the way up the motorway, and on every channel there was the same song.... Cold Play. The words turn round in my head. I didn't even rate Cold Play that much but the words of this song...

I am sure you will know them...

When you try your best but you don't succeed
When you get what you want but not what you need
When you feel so tired you can't sleep
Stuck in Reverse
And the tears come streaming down your face
When you lose something you can't replace
When you love someone but it goes to waste
Could it be worse.....

Lights will guide you Home
And ignite your bones
And I will try to fix you...

I would look after him; I always had. But fixing him without a bit of help was not going to be possible. I know I have been trying for long enough. I do love this man, but hard work really hasn't touched most of the last years.

He had been to our GP and had tried to get help for his problems in the past. It's just his problem is as complex as I said before; manic depression etc and that's just on a good day!

We both know in our hearts this problem has been caused by the time Rex spent in the Army; seeing the things he'd seen. War isn't humane. Being trained the way he was; 'brainwashed' is the word that springs to mind. Leaving that environment without psychological support had triggered this illness; all we needed to do now was get him the right help.

I have worked in mental health and neurobehavioral units; I have watched his illness develop and been unable to help. I think I have managed to help him live with the symptoms for a long time, but obviously without my support and with the attack he had lost the plot. Strangely, he was most definitely calmer than I had seen him in years. It was really quite strange, like he had found some peace in his mind. He reminded me of the description I had once read of a "Neurotic Housewife" in a case study from the seventies, "nicely settled in a world of his own"

The words of the song just swam around in my head.

We arrived home and Dave was waiting up; excited to see his dad. Despite the problems over the years they have remained very close. It was the early hours of Saturday; I knew that I would need to take him into hospital but thought I'd let him chill out at home first. My son and I recognised a much more passive version of the man we had seen go away - and we both just wanted to look after him.

The issues were still there; real in his mind. He knew why he'd left and the fact that he was ill but it seemed he was so stressed about real life he had invented a new one in which we all lived very happily. A new one in which he was a secret agent and many of our friends and family were gods and religious figures; right names, wrong descriptions. Not many religious friends in our circle or saints come to that.

We got him in the bath, in Dave's words he smelt like a "Greek Kebab". You could see him relaxing; but he wasn't sleeping. Cat napping on and off for a few minutes at a time. After a few hours he got up from our bed and went downstairs. He screamed in the toilet; a loud, guttural scream that freaked me out a bit, but he came quietly back to bed after a few minutes. He couldn't sleep but I could tell he was at peace with himself; back near us, his family.
And I could rest, knowing he was safe. But what I had to do next I wasn't convinced would be the best thing for us.

Our local authority doesn't have a good reputation for Mental Health Care; most of my friends who still work in the sector locally have gone to either work in local private hospitals or are doing community support for charities. There is no faith in our local "madhouse".

I tried to get some sleep knowing that getting him into hospital would take time; four to five hours waiting in A&E is about average these days.

It did also cross my mind that the warning from the clairvoyant should have been taken more seriously.

I also always believe things will get better as long as you keep believing; that it will get better one day, *that's why* I choose to be a believer.

Primary what Trust? Who's looking after you?

Saturday looms and I am thinking about getting him to the local NHS drop in centre. I had spoken to our GP the day before; once my brother had told me about his mental state, he advised this was what I should do. It was the bank holiday weekend; we'd been waiting for ages what with all those DIY accidents to contend with.

A lovely Dutch (or Norwegian) Doctor examined Rex at the clinic. Although he could clearly see the evidence of Rex being attacked; the bruising and the cuts, the sores on his feet; he said he could do nothing for his mental health. Rex decided to pull a moony at the doctor as he examined his lower back; the spot where he had been bull whipped. This made us all laugh; he was still very chilled out even though we had already been waiting for an hour and half; he is not normally so good at waiting.

The doctor explained I would need to take him over to casualty; he had arranged for a psychiatrist to meet us there. We had already been a couple of hours and I started to worry about Dave; we had dropped him off at the cinema but he would be coming home soon. I just hoped he had his door key. If not his mate Stevie is round the corner or maybe Char's... I knew he could look after himself; he makes really good egg and oven chips.

A real self-sufficient sixteen year old boy; he can do chicken nuggets and pot noodles too. If he has the energy he can make a yummy stir-fry, but he doesn't have too much energy at sixteen; you know how slow the batteries burn in teenagers...

I had no choice but to take him over to A&E. I knew that he needed some anti-psychotic medication and some sedation to slow him down. He was very calm but he couldn't sit still. So far he was cool but I needed to sleep; we needed some help, so we set of for casualty.

I was amazed at how much he had slowed his thoughts down just in the few hours he had been home; he was slowly coming back down to earth. By this stage I was less concerned about his madness than his physical injuries. I have never seen blisters like the ones he had on his feet.

He reckoned he walked about 20 miles a day for three days in flip-flops... Friends later confirmed this; it seems he was just rushing around constantly on the go since he had been attacked. He also looked a very funny colour; sort of grey with a fantastic tan. Flip-flops and Speedos had been his choice of clothing thus making sure the tan was perfect and line free.

He seemed quite poorly and was eating and drinking strange amounts, gulping down drinks as fast as I could provide them. Then he'd eat and drink nothing for a few hours and then gulp down more; it wasn't like him.

After many hours in A&E the very young psychiatrist (although our local health authority had failed to tell me his name or qualification at this stage- so maybe he wasn't a doctor after all!) decided that my husband was ill and needed sectioning.

They had aimed a lot of questions at Rex and I; we must have told his story about six times to various different people. They had tested his urine for drugs, revealing that slight trace of cannabis. They only conducted this test as Rex had told the young bloke he was a drug baron! He has never in his life taken any other illegal drugs; smoking the occasional spliff was nerve racking enough for him, he has always been too scared to do anything too far outside the law. He had served the Queen too long to break her laws.

I was quite surprised that they wanted to section him; he had come to A&E voluntarily and wasn't causing any problems. I couldn't understand why he wanted to use a section (a piece of paper often referred to as the most powerful piece of paper in the country).

Once you have been sectioned there are many aspects of your life that have to change; they can take your Driving Licence just because you have been sectioned, as we found out; they can make you take treatment or drugs that you don't want to take by force, they can lock you up, shunt you around the country like a piece of meat and deny you basic human rights, just because they use a section...

The "doctor" was very young and obviously not very experienced and, I will admit, obviously very busy.
We had to wait approximately three hours for him to return from an incident on a ward, despite being told by the doctor at the drop in centre that he would be there to meet and greet us. He didn't offer any treatment or advice.

He was the only psychiatric cover in a very busy hospital. When I heard "We'll have to section him" I thought I was hearing things.

The doctor started to blush as I began to point out the facts I knew about the law and using sections, and that I had always believed that sections were for people who "may hurt or be a danger to themselves or others"...
Other than the lack of sleep, he hadn't caused me or anyone else any problems. If you remember he'd had over a week now of being looked after by friends and family, with no problems. The second strong piece of criteria that you must meet is to have "no insight into your illness". That may cause problems but Rex was stood here saying he needed treatment; not denying being ill.

I know you shouldn't say people look young, I was only 37 myself and do not normally look at youth negatively; but this kid in front of me made me want to laugh. I have seen and worked with many assistant psychologists over the years and to be fair some have been fantastic, but I think this one looked like he needed a lot more experience of dealing with people.
I doubted his ability in looking after people when they are so vulnerable. I knew this wasn't right; I could not stand by and watch my husband be locked up. They didn't offer any medication or an informal bed; just to lock him up.

The National Health at it's best! I spoke with the doctor and pointed out he wanted to lock up an innocent, calm man with a mental illness. I asked why he couldn't just be admitted into a ward. The doctor went into a long explanation about having no beds; if you need a bed they have to get you one, if you're sectioned, it's a "duty of care" thing. Once they have detained you it's their responsibility; they lock you up to get you a bed, not because you're mad enough to need "sectioning".

Eventually he agreed that I could take Rex home for the night and that he would find a bed for the next day. There really was no evidence that he needed locking up.

He couldn't give us one good reason for keeping Rex locked up; he clearly wasn't a danger to anyone.

Guilty as charged for being in the army; fighting wars that weren't his. Being a good man; a good provider. Hard working, tax-paying citizen and now they want to lock him up because he's gone a bit mad? What an attitude. Lock him up? Terrorists, drug dealers, paedophiles, fraudsters, killers; all on the loose, but let's lock up this vulnerable person because he's gone a bit bonkers and they don't have facilities to look after him.

What a bloody joke.

I think the doctor took one look at him and made an assumption that he was trouble. He looks the part; he's only 5'9 but he is a bit stocky, shaved head, you know the type. The man was clearly scared of his own shadow; he just kept blushing as he couldn't answer my questions.

Like I said before the government figures show that one in four people suffer from mental health problems; so why don't they have to have enough beds to be able to look after people when they need it.

And worst of all, these poor people, not just my husband have to be sectioned and detained to get care; that has got to be inhumane. Can you just imagine if the NHS said they had to lock up cancer patients or expectant mothers to provide them with the treatment they need?

So anyway, off home again it was clear no one else would do anything for this ill man other than lock him up. They had made their only offer of help. So once again I had to take him home to look after him.

We arranged to go back to the hospital for 10am the next day. The doctor said they would have a bed ready.

The night was lovely, and very peaceful. Looking after him was funny, Dave and I were laughing about some of the stuff that he was coming out with. If you listened carefully, and knew him, you could seriously understand what he was saying; it all made sense.

He had a lot on his mind before he went away; his family, relationships, his parents, and sister especially. He had a niece that he didn't meet until just before he went away. Her name is Eden. He spoke a lot about the Garden of Eden; which sounded all strange and biblical but it was clear to us he was trying to work out his feelings for his niece. Other things made sense too; I was Mother Earth, anyone who knows me will laugh about this bit. I just think he needed someone to cling to and I was that person again. I am not mother earth; I buy takeaways and cook lunch on a Sunday, that's about my limit!

His time in the army had left him with this illness; brainwashing for 14 years, trained in an extreme, controlled environment; not to think or feel too much emotion just to fight and be a soldier. All sounds like professional grooming to me.

Once again that's a hindsight thing. At the time, life in the Army felt normal; yet looking back it was far from it. When he left he did just 2 weeks resettlement; Rex chose to do a computer course. With no emotional support or de-briefing taking place, he was just sent out into the world with all his ghosts and fears. And with several active tours under his belt; that is quite a lot of emotional baggage to carry.

I do know it affects a lot of soldiers to varying degrees but the government are still trying to deny it exists. Recently they were put on the spot when I read they had sent 900 people to the Priory in the last year.

I am sure those getting into the Priory are probably officers or maybe people from the TA. Again I read somewhere in an article saying it's easier to prove Post Traumatic Stress for people in the TA, and with more people being called up into active duty, many more TA volunteers are being affected by this disabling illness.

The reason for the quicker, easier diagnosis of Post Traumatic Stress for "part-timers" is due to the fact that they can easily prove they were coping well "mentally" before their deployment into active duty. You know bank managers, doctors, lawyers, all kinds of people sign up for the TA; I am sure that most have never expected to be at war but it's happening all the time these days...

Some part-time recruits are doing a lot of active duties. One of our senior managers has been on active duty for a big chunk of the year; some other friends have done several tours over the last years.

I believe regular soldiers are thin on the ground. I spoke to an old mate who has just left the army himself; he said that plenty of people are still joining up; unfortunately retaining young soldiers seems to be the issue.

Working in the social sector with the client groups that I do means I am often coming across people who have done a few years in the army, then left due to the institution and the amount of active duty they are expected to do. Far too stressful for most people I should think.

Mostly, young men are sent to war zones within twelve months of completing their training, most under 19 years old.

I vow to find out exactly how many people this is affecting; just to shame the government.

My poor old man gave fourteen years to the regulars, and most of his mates did at least that time too, many completing the twenty-two years that the army liked.

We have had to fight to prove what has caused his illness and have put up with a health service that has been unable to treat it, despite several government targets being set for specialist treatment to be made available locally for these war veterans.

Life would be so easy if we could just say he was ok six months ago, like the "TA" soldiers can, but his exposure to the environment went on for years, from the tender age of sixteen.

Anyway, Rex didn't have the 'Priory' clinic or any specialist care; he just had little old me; all I could do was my best to look after him.

It was a peaceful night. He still didn't sleep well but was calm, yet mad, but settled with no shouting. I bet if you ask our neighbours they would testify to this. I must admit at 4am I made him take two herbal sleeping tablets, just to just try and get a little bit of sleep. I was expecting another long day at the hospital and he needed to rest.

We had been able to provide good information for the doctors to start working on and I hoped they would look after him. I had worked in Mental Health services for four years in our city and had met staff from our local ward at training events and stuff. The hospital's reputation wasn't that good but I had to hope that the young doctor had sorted it all out; a bed on a ward where they could start some drug treatment until they could organise therapy to help him long term, they could look after him better than me; they were professionals.

My mind was whizzing with thoughts; I was sure he just needed some mood stabiliser, or anti-psychotic medication to slow him down; surely they could sort that out today?

I made him eggs on toast and we got ready to go back to the hospital. Dave told Rex that he'd use his bike to come and see him everyday; the hospital was only two miles at the most from our house.

We all hoped that Rex was going to get better at last. The sun was shining and I hoped it would be a good day. I was quite tired and stressed; it was only a week ago my doctor was telling me to take time off to recuperate myself; now I was looking after Rex again...

A proper diagnosis, and the right treatment and at last we could start to live with this illness, instead of it taking over as it had done for the last few years.

We headed back down to the hospital, getting there for about 10.30am Sunday morning. Not a big surprise, but the doctor was missing again. We waited for two hours before he turned up; he asked a couple of questions, it was the strangest assessment of an illness I had ever witnessed.

They had tested him for drugs the night before; showing a slight trace of cannabis... so the first suggestions were obviously it must be drug-induced psychosis. Rex talked to the doctor honestly and openly about his use of cannabis; he had nothing to hide. He had used it occasionally; he knew now that it wasn't what had caused these problems; so he told the doctor straight.

So to measure how ill he was, the doctor asked him two questions about proverbs. One of the questions was "what do you understand about the proverb a bird in the hand is worth two in the bush?" I still don't know how that was appropriate, but it makes me smile.

I nearly started laughing; Rex was being very sarcastic. Even in his mad state he knew this guy was no more a doctor than I am a super model.

Just to give you an idea of the likelihood of that; Bridget's pants would have been extremely tight...if I could have even fitted in them!!

It was then he said he was going to sort out a bed. I wondered why this wasn't sorted out already; hadn't we had given them plenty of time to find a bed?

It was well past lunchtime before we got upstairs to the ward; it was in an attic and was filthy. The ward looked like a dumping ground for old furniture. We were asked to sit in a corridor whilst the nurses did handover. I could hear every word they were saying about my husband and the other patients on the ward. I felt unnerved by my surroundings, but I kept Rex amused whilst we waited for them to sort him out.

I started to regret bringing him; I should have got a GP to come and prescribe some medication at home. To be honest I needed a break; it was going to take time to fix him; he was pretty jumbled up, but this dark, horrid ward was extremely glum. I didn't want to leave him but I knew I had to; this was all that was on offer. It was very dirty but we both knew he needed some treatment.

They gave him some medication and showed us to a room. It looked a bit like a big cell with a dirty little shower room partitioned off to one side.

One of the staff on the ward recognised me from some training we'd done together a few years before.
We started to talk; catching up about people we knew and as we chatted I told all about Rex's past. I relaxed; he had taken some medication as we arrived and I felt sure they could look after him. He was calm and chilled out; I left him laid on the bed. I thought he might go to sleep.
I told the nurse in charge to ring me if there were any problems; I was only 10 minutes from the hospital and would go back if they needed me to. I know wards are often short staffed and he'd need a lot of care; he was physically poorly as well as mentally distressed.

I left the hospital at 4pm and went home to see Dave; we needed to have something to eat and I needed to make sure he was ok. He is a cool kid but this had been a full on weekend for us all.

I had told the staff to call me if Rex started getting upset; I knew he would get stroppy; asking to know where I was. He had needed to know where I was and when he would next see me; this had been constant for the past three years. I told them all about it, it had driven me mad in the past but as he was ill and he might need me, they agreed they would ring if he got upset or anxious about anything.

At this stage I thought he was going to be looked after; yet I still cried all the way home. I am very proud of him, he is my husband, and after what this government has put him through, using him as a soldier in their war games, and then our years of struggling, trying to get him help; I just hoped our local hospital could look after him.

I did have my doubts, hence the tears. However, as the staff nurse was ex forces, I pinned my hope on the fact that he would have some level of understanding about this illness.

I also knew that Rex was not the only ex-soldier in our city needing treatment for this specific illness; there are several army camps locally. A lot of squaddies settle down in this area; I know of several others with varying degrees of this illness that have been admitted to our hospital, so I assumed they must have a little experience.

The question was how much did they care? Soon, I was going to find out the answer.

Nightmare

To be honest, I was surprised not to hear from them. I knew how ill he was and how disorientated he would be in strange surroundings. After just a couple of hours I thought I'd ring to find out how he was doing; I was just about to drink the large glass of wine I had poured myself to try and relax. It had been a long weekend but I knew I should ring before I made myself incapable of driving.

I was sure it would be ok; they would have rung if there was a problem, so you can imagine I was quite surprised when the staff nurse answered the phone and said he was shouting and being aggressive. I was shocked because that wasn't the way he had been since the attack some ten days earlier, he had been a little delusional and calm when I left him.

They had only been looking after him, or should I say he had been in their care for just a smidge over two and a half hours.

I asked what had wound him up and but the guy didn't respond. I wanted to go check it out, so I suggested that I could come down and see what was happening; to see if I could calm him down. The nurse replied that it might help if I did.

I didn't want to think of him upset and distressed; he was ill. So I set off; ten or fifteen minutes later I arrived at the hospital.

As I arrived I noticed the police going in the same direction; nothing new, there is often police at hospitals these days. I didn't even notice they were heading in the same direction and eventually, same destination as me. A police officer was already in the ward as I walked in. Again I ignored the fact; never in a million years thinking that they were there for Rex.

I asked the nurse what was happening; he said Rex had pulled a radiator off the wall and threatened to strangle the doctor. Strangely, he hadn't mentioned this on the phone.

As I went into the small area that contained the office, and a small dirty smoking room I could hear he was shouting; obviously very distressed.

I started to speak to him; he stopped shouting and calmed down almost instantly; starting to talk to me.

I was upset by the state of him; he had only been there three hours and they had not done anything to start treating him; something had obviously distressed him. I expected to feel scared; I have seen this man in many situations over the last twenty years and can read him like a book (definitely easier than reading or writing this book!) and I didn't feel that he was being particularly aggressive; very loud but not intimidating. I knew him though, I am sure that makes a big difference, but I had been able to tell them what to expect. I am sure I had told them he was a big-gobbed softy - they obviously hadn't listened.

I sat with him for a few minutes. A member of staff was stood outside the door; he was happy for me to be in the room and never asked me to leave. As I tried to speak to him the staff member couldn't look at me, I tried to find out what had happened; little did I know I was about to find out.

Within a few minutes the police officer I had seen in the corridor came into the room, three more quickly followed. The room was about 8ft by 8ft, they were all dressed in body armour and a couple had riot shields. I noticed the one advancing towards him, his mace at the ready. I was pushed into the corridor as they moved into restrain him. I have never found out what had happened to warrant this restraint but I will…

I stood by, horrified and helpless. I could here him screaming for me, my brother and son. The people who loved him and had been able to look after him, but now the police were pinning him down. He was screaming he couldn't breathe, I also heard him pleading for someone to remove their knee from against his neck.

I could hear them; they were hand cuffing him. Then one of the officers came out and got leg restraints; they were putting shackles on his ankles.

I thought I was going to faint, I have never fainted, so I don't know that's what was going to happen, but my head was reeling, I felt sick and hot. I like to be a little dramatic so pretending to faint is the only dramatic bit I have allowed myself in the book, the rest of it is fact.

It was like a scene from 'Street Crime UK', but this wasn't some criminal committing some dodgy crime, this was my husband, and he was supposed to be in hospital being treated for an illness, an illness as common as a cold.

This ward was a six bed ward, the only provision in our area for looking after the most acute, mentally ill patients but now they were saying that they couldn't even look after my husband. A man who has lived within the community with this illness for six years, with very little help or support from the professionals in the health service. In fact the consultant had made it worse when he first met him in 2003 by telling him he wasn't ill; he was just a druggie.

I'd seen worse behaviour in the street with no arrests being made on nights out.

My mind also flashed back; remembering an incident that happened a few years ago when a big guy in one of the private units where I was working went ballistic, attacking people, smashing the place up and causing no end of problems. The police had attended our ward to see what was happening but they refused to do anything; they wouldn't even come onto the ward. This guy was sectioned in a private hospital so they wouldn't touch him; he had injured staff, attacking them physically.

The police were happy for us to continue to look after him because he wasn't a danger to anyone except the staff and residents within our unit. The police left him with us, basically telling us to get on with it, and he was really dangerous. They had already bought extra staff on to the ward and there was still enough risk to us for us to call the police; we had tried to manage his behaviours for days before we called them in.

That was a private hospital not far from our local hospital; all I could think was that the staff had lied about his level of aggression; for this to be done by the same police force in this way. Or maybe the local PCT have an agreement with the police to look after ill patients in this way; to make life easier for NHS staff.

I was instantly annoyed when discovering they must have organised this before I'd called them to find out how he was doing, I immediately felt like I had been used by the hospital staff as a decoy to distract him, whilst the police got into position.

My experience of working in places like this had always been that who ever had the best rapport with a client would deal with them when they were in crisis; they obviously thought I would be the best option for the minimal amount of fuss, considering the actions they had decided to take, the decision that was supposedly best for my husband.

After about ten minutes of being restrained they carried my poor man out, face down like a bag of shit and with no shoes on his feet; he just had a pair of shorts on.

Face down, screaming, crying and very distressed. I watched in disbelief. I stormed up to the hospital staff and into their office.

The staff nurse explained to me that the qualified staff in an acute ward for people with mental health problems could not look after such a violent man. The staff nurse explained he was being taken to the police station at the hospital's request as a place of safety; there would be no charges against him, from there he would quickly be taken to an appropriate bed "somewhere" as soon as possible.

I asked what an appropriate bed was; he'd always managed to sleep in a bed as long as I known him.

You know the type; we have had divans, wooden bed steads. We have slept in four-posters, single beds, double beds and a couple of years ago we even treated ourselves to a king size luxury orthopaedic... he has spent a lot of time in tents and roughing it on tours for the Army; any bed would do for him. To be honest, it's one thing he has never been fussy about.

In this situation, as far as I could see it was the care that had obviously been the problem, not the bed, what did they mean by appropriate?

The nurse mentioned that the police station was being used as a place of safety my mental health training kicked in, I asked what section they were going to use. It was clear that is what they were going to do; use a section to detain him just like they had wanted the day before.

I asked where the information that he was violent came from; I have never seen him fight or hit anyone else in the twenty years I have known him, never.
The nurse repeated the story; that he had ripped a radiator off the wall and threatened to strangle the doctor, who by now I felt sure was neither qualified appropriately or experienced enough to be in charge of such a demanding, alleged high risk situation.

If the assessment I had witnessed was anything to go by I could imagine what it had been like on that ward for the last couple of hours; the guy was scared of his own shadow, so my chunky-looking man must have scared his pants off with his mad threats. Even now he was cowering in the corner of the room, leaving the 6ft shithouse built nurse to do most of the talking. I am only five foot four; hardly look like the type of woman who would start beating up doctors. But he was clearly scared.
I knew via the big nurse he had taught control and restraint for nursing staff for many years; I had done the training and refresher courses

over the years, I had worked locally. A good source of income for local PCT'S is selling this sort of training to private hospitals for their staff; it is common practice, a nice little money spinner.

The first and last lessons were that you couldn't restrain people without good reason i.e. they had physically attacked someone or had made extremely serious threats, or had a past that would lead you to believe that they would carry out their threats. Had he thrown the radiator at someone or gone for the doctor? I could understand them stopping it but to get the police to do this over a few words and a decrepit old radiator was ridiculous.

There was no evidence of aggression, no police record, not even known to the police, he had not hurt or harmed anyone. So why the dramatic restraint?

I knew the answer, and so did they. It was JUST for being mad; the local authority failing to provide adequate treatment. The start of the suitable bed battle was about to begin.
I had taken him home and looked after him single handed, with no formal training and a sixteen year old kid as back up to give them time to find that "appropriate suitable" bed…

As I stood there, it looked and felt to me like serious abuse of a vulnerable adult that I had stupidly left in their hands.

I lost my rag eventually, and started to argue with them as I got them to pack all of Rex's belongings. The hospital bed manager came into the ward, I suppose she could be a very nice woman normally, but my encounter with her that day was worse than crap.

I asked her what they intended to do with Rex to which she responded she didn't have any idea, but she would need to find him a bed somewhere. She really didn't seem that interested in Rex; he had become a problem to her and she didn't hide it, but this had only happened because the bloody hospital staff couldn't look after him.

That wasn't his fault, he didn't come to hospital for shit care, but she seemed to think the problem was Rex and was very negative about him and his illness.

I felt very angry and frustrated, but what could I do? I had worked with the mental health system in this country for years, I knew he would now be sectioned and it would be out of my hands. I knew the procedure, I knew they were in charge of him now.

The hospital that was, not the police. I knew they were being directed by the nursing staff, but it did amaze and alarm me that they hadn't needed to witness or have any evidence of any serious crime to detain someone like that. What about human rights?

Only hospital staff witnessed the alleged threat to strangle the doctor and the serious abuse of a radiator...

And to be honest I know that can't be classed as a public order offence against someone being treated for mental health problems in a hospital ward or at least I hope I know that…Rex has never been charged with any offence, so…I can only conclude that the police did take him from that hospital illegally, he wasn't detained under the mental health act until he was at the police station and he wasn't arrested at the hospital. Scary what they can do to you without good reason or evidence in this country isn't it?

We have lived with this illness for years and looked after him for the last 48 hours without medical training or medication; I truly couldn't understand how they had failed to look after him for a few hours. Now he was being taken to a police cell, with no medical care being provided to him, just a police cell to be locked up in and police officers to look after him.

By this stage they could give me no indication of their plans to look after him or treat him. I blew my stack.

As I started to leave the ward I remember using some choice language… And I promised to come back and throttle the 'doctor' myself!

I saw him a few weeks ago, the young guy; the 'doctor'. He was buying pictures in our local Dunhelm store, as he saw me come around the corner he looked like a rabbit caught in headlights.
I smiled as he put his picture down, grabbed his girlfriend's hand and ran for the exit. Dave and Rex laughed when I told them, but to be honest I felt extremely sick. What had he done to my husband that day in the hospital? He certainly looked sheepish when he realised he was face to face with me months later…
I waited in the ward as they got his stuff. Unable to control my anger and frustration I shouted at them, but no police officers violently restrained me at the request of hospital staff. It is truly amazing what they think they can get away with as 'care' for mad people. How many people does this happen to across the country everyday I wonder? Not everyone has people who care like Rex, and even less with knowledge of patient's rights and the mental health system.

I walked away from the ward for the second time that day with tears streaming down my face; a young policeman walked passed me and said "it's all right love". He walked to the van, like that would make me feel better! I suppose he tried to make me feel better, he cared a bit, and that was a bit more than the hospital staff had done.

I walked passed the police van that held my husband; could not help but look, the van was rocking and I could hear him screaming, my heart breaking as I knew this stocky, well-built softy was going to be scared to death by the situation he was in.

Despite the assessment and assumptions made by the staff in that ward that afternoon, I knew he wasn't a violent criminal or thug; he is a man with an illness. They seemed to have forgotten the attack and his apparent sunstroke. I was worrying about things like his severe dehydration, a possible head injury, he did have a faded bruise on his face - you could tell how big it had been when it had been fresh; it clearly must have been quite a blow he had sustained, not to mention his severe apparent mental distress that could have been bought about by any one of these incidents. His history of poor mental health should have also been considered, but they had clearly been too busy labelling him dangerous and unmanageable to have had time to try looking after him as well.

I wanted to go and start on the policeman in the van, but I knew it was the hospital's fault, not the police.

As I walked to my car I wondered who had been looking after Rex whilst the hospital staff had been busy inventing a violent person who needed locking up.

Who was going to look after him now, give him medication and water, not a police officer, surely they are needed for catching real criminals?

I drove home to find a note from Dave saying he had gone to see his friend Char; she had first hand experience of mental illness; her Granny had spent many years in and out of the same hospital that Rex was in now and he obviously needed some support.

They have been best friends for years, she was Dave's first girlfriend and after they split up they realised they had to stay friends, they are still friends; I think they always will be. They are like peas in a pod. The odd couple; Char's mum often laughs at them as they sit end to end, bitching about stuff, tonight they were plotting to break her Granny and his dad out of the local hospital; this was suggested by Dave. He knew the hospital had a bad reputation and after she had explained in detail that her granny's brain had been fried over the years by compulsive ECT (Electro Convulsive Treatment), they came up with a plan. Chars granny has a long history of depression for which ECT can be prescribed; in some cases from what I have read it can help, but only in the most extreme cases. It wasn't the right thing for Dave to hear on that day though, but I knew that she just wanted to help. Their relationship had always thrived on her outrageous stories; he always came home with tales from Charlotte that made me chuckle…

107

Another part I just thought about; this is approximately my tenth proof read of this bit of the book, I am sure there was an article in the local news about a year ago about our newly refurbished, all singing and dancing, state of the art, electro convulsive treatment suite or whatever it is called, had been used over three hundred times in a year. Most other hospitals licensed to use this, often referred to as barbaric treatment, would expect to use it maybe fifty times in a year. So maybe Charlotte wasn't exaggerating as much as I suggested to Dave at the time. Or maybe that's something else that our local hospital flogs on to other authorities to make money, making its usage appear high for our local area?

We know how much our hospitals spend, we know how much they claim to get from the government, but who knows how much they make on flogging stuff? Expensive equipment can pay for itself over and over again in situations like this, so they must get quite an income if that's the rate they can sell NHS resources…

Anyway, despite the fact that he was at Chars, and quite likely hatching plans or being scared to death, to be honest it suited me that he was out; as I sat down and rang my brother.

My head was reeling; I didn't know what to do. But I was lucky, I had many friends to turn to who worked in this field, who could advise me what to do next. I knew in my heart that all I could do was sit and wait for a call from an approved social worker, probably after hours of waiting. I'd been in this situation many times before, just not with my husband, and unfortunately I knew how long the wait could be.

My brother listened in horror at my account of what had happened, and calmed me down. We talked it through; how he had been on the flight and stuff like that. Yeah he'd been a bit grumpy, but no major aggressive outbursts, yes I wasn't going mad Fred had managed to look after him for four days. He had managed to transport him halfway across Europe with only the aid of friends and Easy Jet.

I had looked after him peacefully at home for the best part of two days; only with the aid of our sixteen year old son.

It seemed surreal this was happening, we talked through the options. It didn't take long as there wasn't that many open to us. All we could come up with was keeping friendly with the custody sergeant at the police station. At least that way, we could find out how he was doing and I was fast learning that the police are better onside, than off in these situations.

So I rang the police station, and they confirmed he was being held there with no charge against him; that they would now need to wait for the doctors and local authority to sort out where he was going.

I asked them how long this might take in their experience; they couldn't give me any idea, just saying he hoped it would be soon as clearly he was a very ill man.

I got numbers for the hospital bed manager and social services, I tried calling but it seemed no one could tell me what they were going to do for him, my ill husband.

They seemed to have no urgency, he was locked in a police cell, and he wasn't going anywhere; why should they rush?

By the time Dave came home a couple of hours later I had managed to calm myself down. I was on my second large glass of wine. I don't really drink that much anymore; I used to drink like a fish on nights out but over the last few years, since the issues with Rex drinking, I don't enjoy it that much. In the old days he would, and has, carried me home miles after nights out; for the first thirteen years of our life together that was standard practice. Then we went through a few years where I couldn't drink if he was; scared of being out of control when drunk in case he kicked off and I had to calm him down... That night I didn't even taste it, I just tipped it down my throat, wanting it to fuddle my brain so I didn't have to think about what was happening.

I didn't want to have to tell Dave the details, I thought by time he gets up tomorrow I can tell him they had just moved his dad to another hospital for better care; he would never need to know what I had seen. He is just as protective of his dad as I am, probably more so actually. I knew this would upset him. I just hoped our local hospital found somewhere quickly so that he could be looked after, I couldn't rest knowing that he was locked in a cell. I felt sick just thinking how much I knew this would be making Rex worse; panic attacks and anxiety had been major problems; being detained would be causing both, but for Dave's sake I had to cope and keep it together.

I sat with Dave, pretending all was well and talking things through with him. It had been a bonkers weekend that had turned nasty, and I knew it. So when the phone rang I pounced on it. It was just before eleven, nearly four hours since they had taken him away; it was a social worker asking to speak to me.

I got Dave to go upstairs, I think he knew something was happening but I was sure he didn't need to hear the details.

The call was about being Rex's closest relative, she started to explain how they wanted to section him using section 2 of the Mental Health Act; like I said I have heard it all before, but the social worker obviously didn't know that.

This would allow them to assess his needs whilst keeping him locked up for up to 28 days. She never mentioned the negative side effects of using it, or the power that it gave them, just that they had the power to use it as they saw fit.

I said that I didn't agree; that he shouldn't be sectioned; he walked into a hospital asking for help...
If he lacked insight into what his problem was, as she was describing it, had only occurred in the few hours they looked after him at that hospital. Prior to that Rex and I had spent fourteen hours out of the last twenty four in the hospital together asking the doctors for treatment.

He had defiantly realised what his problems were when I left him on the ward.

I asked what section had been used to take him from the hospital to the police station, I suspected that this hadn't been done inline with the law but I didn't want to push it until I had checked my facts. Removing a person to a place of safety was covered by something other than a section two I was sure. She became very patronising, asking me why I was asking, I didn't say anything, I needed to check my facts. She quickly went on to say that this was a courtesy call really, just to inform me of what they were doing and that she didn't have to answer my questions.
She stated again that he was a danger to himself and others and that he would be sectioned in the next few hours. Reassurance for relatives clearly wasn't her strong point.

He had been locked up for well over three hours already, I asked her to get on and do it so that he could be moved to a hospital and be looked after; that is all I wanted for him.
I also asked her to let me know when and where he was going. It was well past 11 now. He'd been in that cell or taken away shackled at about 7.15pm; he was psychically ill as well as mad, as I kept pointing out.

My phone didn't stop ringing; I'd only told my brother and sister Mandy, and one or two close friends that I had called for advice. But as it approached the early hours of the morning on Bank holiday Monday I knew he was still locked in that police cell. I couldn't stop being sick; I had stopped drinking after the third glass so it wasn't the drink. I had scared myself a little, feeling like I wanted to drink like that; the family curse passed down from my old drunk Dad was never far from my thoughts... I think I was in shock.

I tried the hospital and social services again but they had not found a bed for him. I got a blanket and lay on the sofa, people had offered to come round but I didn't want Dave to know what had happened; so best to keep it as normal as possible. By the time he got up I was sure I could cover up what I'd seen.

They just needed to get him into hospital. What about his sunstroke, dehydration etc? Police cells don't come with psychiatric care. Or nurses. Police officers should be fighting crime, doing police stuff, not looking after mentally ill patients.

Dave is only sixteen and some things are too much, he has dealt with a lot, watching his dad go slowly mad over the last few years but amazingly he does have a well-balanced attitude. But what had happened was horrendous, anyone that knows Rex would never have believed that there was a need for what I had witnessed.

I could have talked him into anything if they had given me chance but obviously they just wanted rid of him.

He knows me, trusts and loves me, but they hadn't given me time to do anything at the hospital, in fact as I looked back I couldn't even understand why the staff nurse had said come in, unless I was the decoy.

They had obviously decided to have him taken to the police station; so why call me in to witness what they had done?

We all know the police don't often turn up within 10 minutes, especially when they are coming into restrain someone in full riot gear. They didn't even ask him to leave peacefully; they had come to restrain him. The staff must have arranged it all before I even rang; my head was whizzing with all of these thoughts as the hours ticked by.

I had to consider everything and Dave was about to start his GCSE'S; I had to keep him in the dark, he didn't needed the extra stress.

I tried to sleep but every time I closed my eyes I could see him, hear him screaming for us three as the police had carried him out of that dirty shit hole they have the front to call a hospital. One saving grace was that the cell was probably cleaner...

I couldn't sleep. I think I must have catnapped for a few minutes on and off but by six in the morning I was sat drinking tea, my head exploding. I wanted to ring to see if he had been taken to a hospital but at the same time I was scared of knowing that he was still locked up in that cell.

I have worked with many people in mental distress and of course things can get out of hand quickly without the right treatment. He was obviously unwell, that is why I took him to hospital in the first place. I knew he needed medication to slow down his thoughts and his mind, and medical care but they were denying him it at this crucial time. I began to wish I'd never bloomin taken him.

I knew that if he was still locked up in the cell he would be in a bad way by now. The army had looked after him, then I had looked after him and now, with all due respect to the police, I just knew in my heart that no one was looking after him.

I rang the hospital and the approved social worker again; I was right, he was still locked up in the cell. I began to shake, my sick husband had been locked up for nearly twelve hours and neither the hospital manager nor the social worker could confirm who was responsible for his welfare or care.
Both admitted to me that keeping him locked up this way was not acceptable but neither seemed in a rush to get a hospital to look after him.

I asked for them to arrange for me to go to the police station to see him myself. They both said I couldn't see him. I wondered why I couldn't see my sick husband; he'd been sectioned for assessment in hospital last night and today I still couldn't get to see him because he's in a cell, not a hospital bed? They really were in control. He'd had no medical attention for twelve hours, just a police doctor who was probably rushed off his feet.

I woke my brother in tears. I have never felt so useless in my life. I had taken him to be cared for and no one seemed to care except me. I didn't expect them to fall over themselves rushing, but this was a joke.

My brother said ring the police station direct again and see how he's doing. The custody sergeant had changed and this time I spoke to a woman; she was lovely, trying to reassure me as much as she could. She said they were looking after him as best they could but they weren't qualified.

She also confirmed that I couldn't go to the police station but said that they would keep me informed as they hoped he would be moved soon. I think "too ill" to be in a police station was mentioned.

I didn't feel much better but I did feel the police cared about what was happening.

I felt sick in my stomach that I had taken him to a hospital to be looked after and that this was the result, he locked in a police station a few miles from me with no one to look after him, me going out of my head with worry.

I prayed that the teenager would do the teenage thing and stay in bed till midday; it was only eight in the morning, so it went through my mind that this could still be resolved before he had to find out.

Ten o'clock and still no news; I got back on the phone but this time there was news. They think they may have founds a bed; in Liverpool. 110 miles away.

I was concerned about the distance for about two seconds, it didn't matter; it was a hospital. Someone would look after him this time, I hoped.

I asked when they would be taking him so I could go over to Liverpool and see that he was ok with my own eyes.

They told me it wasn't confirmed yet as the hospital was waiting for a more senior manager to come in. I knew that meant an expensive hospital, they would need to agree funding. This has happened in hospitals before when I have been working in the past. At last it was getting sorted. They said they'd be in touch very soon.

By twelve still no more news, the hours were ticking by slowly and I rang the hospital again, this time speaking to the senior manager. I was losing my temper; it seems they still hadn't got him on his way to the hospital. I was starting to lose my cool and raise my voice just as Dave walked down the stairs… They had agreed the funding and were just waiting for transport, I asked how long that might take and once again I got no commitment.

I put the phone down thinking that this was just a farce; that I'd try the police again. They had been the best of the professionals I'd been dealing with in the 17 hours he had been locked up in that police cell. But then they probably needed the cell to deal with criminals, so they would want rid of him.

I spoke to the policewoman again; she informed me they were transporting him in a police van due to wanting him out of the cells. They were going to do it within the next hour. They couldn't wait any longer for the ambulance that had been promised by the hospital.

I got hold of the hospital manager who confirmed that was happening, and confirmed the name of the hospital he was going to. He had been locked at that police cell for nineteen hours. The last twenty four hours had been a surreal event; like a living nightmare. He was going to a hospital at last but too late to protect my kid from this terrible event, days before the most important examinations of his life.

I had to tell Dave; he stood in the doorway staring at me, looking very grown up and demanding to know what's happening.
I explained to him what had happened, keeping it as light as it could be when it's your dad you're being told about.

He got upset but fast became angry like me. I hate to say it but I think we are both overprotective of Rex, but I honestly think that is because he has become so vulnerable over the last years; lack of treatment and understanding of this Post Traumatic Stress stuff has ruined all of our lives to some extent. It's only natural to want your relative; husband, brother, sister, dad or whoever, treated with dignity and respect when they are ill; that's why we were both angry.

I went upstairs and used the internet to locate the hospital that was to be my husband's destination. It took about two minutes; I do still wonder why it took so long, with advance technology like the internet for the hospital to find it, they must keep a list.

I found the website; it looked like a nice place. I decided to ring them. I got through to a very friendly receptionist who said she'd locate someone to talk to me.

A bright Scottish voice came on the line, a nurse called Gordon.
I started to talk and couldn't stop, Gordon encouraged me to talk. He wanted to get as much information as he could and I was so relieved to talk to a nurse who seemed to want to help my husband.
Something in his voice made me feel at ease and I started to ask for directions, he told me I shouldn't go over that night.

I began to panic again I needed to know he was alright. I quickly explained that he had no shoes and clothes. I told him about the sun stroke, and food and water would definitely be needed, oh and fags.

Gordon told me to calm down and chuckled as he said they were capable of looking after Rex, yes they did know that patients needed food and water!
I don't know why, with my fast growing mistrust of health professionals I believed him. He promised to ring me back as soon as Rex got there and they had him settled.

I sat down and cried for the first time in the past three days. My friend Lisa had arrived and was busy ordering pizza. It felt like the last hours had been like the twilight zone, or a bad nightmare. But somehow I knew I could trust this nurse that had promised to look after him.

I couldn't decide if my knowledge and background in mental health environments, both working in secure wards and in the community, had helped or hindered me; but it had made me pushy and demanding. I dread to think how long he'd have been in that cell for if I hadn't been around to stick up for him, nagging them to get him moved.

I cried and cried and cuddled Dave. I was an emotional wreck but at least people cared, the phone started ringing again...
I still had only told a couple of people and now they could come round; seeing the look on their faces as they listened to the whole story, the anger started to bubble inside me. How it had this got to this point was still beyond me.

True to his word Gordon rang and told me Rex had arrived, was very poorly, but he would be ok and that I should come over the next day. They were going to sedate him. It was clear he hadn't slept for days and Gordon swore by a goodnights sleep.

My mind at rest we ate the pizza and my friend Lisa stayed over, insisted on driving me over to the hospital the next day. I was thankful for her help.

I went to bed and slept in fits and starts. I don't know about post traumatic stress but what I had seen in that hospital was going to give me nightmares for weeks. It must surely be a psychological reaction to an extreme stressor don't you think...

Again I thought of what had brought my family to this point; I can only blame the army in the first instance, and the failure of the local health service to diagnose and treat him quickly at the first sign of symptoms years ago, having left the army he should have fallen into a high risk of mental health problems group and treated as such.

He had held it together for a long time, but most people who knew him knew a breakdown of some sort would come one day.

He had managed to cope right up until he walked out of his job; although I couldn't blame him; they had rubbished his illness and made him even more unable to cope with life. What with his yard manager making jokes about his illness, how could he have stayed?

In real terms at that stage we were better off than we'd ever been; more money, our own home, two cars - a nice lifestyle. But it hadn't made us happy, or made any difference to Rex's mental health. That had got steadily worse as our lives got better.
Lots of friends and family looked into our lives, finding it hard to understand how this could happen to us; they would look at us and think we had everything.
I didn't understand it enough to stop it from happening. I have only understood some parts of this since I started writing the book. Looking at things in black and white can make more sense of stuff than you can ever imagine so I can't blame them for not understanding. I had helped him to cover it up for the most part, understanding his embarrassment at people knowing he had gone mad.
To be fair there is still a lot of stigma and lack of understanding involved in having mental health problems. Not everyone can be "Mad and proud". It can feel like having a giant wart on your nose even though you know people can't see it.

At least this bank holiday was coming to an end, I was exhausted and stressed, and ready for some sleep.

I had a feeling Gordon was going to be a big help.

From starting to write this book a couple of months after Rex came out of hospital I gave myself a year to finish it. Life has turned into a battle in many respects this week; we have just won a battle with the DVLA, they tried to take his licence for three years; he ended up just loosing it for a month. The reason for the stress; just four months after he had been so ill? - Because his consultant made a mistake. Had I not been around to support him that could put him back no end, causing more stress, they seem to enjoy causing more stress than necessary for my husband.

Whilst I am on "the local health service" they still haven't provided any treatment for him; all is not lost because we managed to get some private treatment. But is that the right way to have to look after your mad relative? To put someone through this sort of forced assessment months ago then still end up with no proper treatment is like taking a scan of a tumour and not even trying to remove it.

As I sit writing this it is not long til Christmas; I need to get going. I promised myself a new life this year, and so far have only got three weeks peace. I haven't even seen a beach this year, so I need to sell a few books to make sure I have money for a holiday next year! I told you Bridget Jones had it easy; at least she got trips with her job. I commute an hour a day, each way to work and back on the M1, that's the most travel I do these days...

Last Christmas I promised myself a new job and sometime off to lie on the beach. This coming year, I am going to get what I want, even if I have to sell him to a white slaver to get it! Man for sale, fluent in Morse code and English....

I was also trying to make sure this is going to be a good Christmas. Things are getting better and it will be a nice way to start a new year. Rex having his breakdown at the beginning of May triggered several events that have made 2006 one of the worst.
I am ever the optimist though, and as I sit writing I know that life has certainly been a lot worse than it is right now. The weekend when I took him to hospital is still haunting me, six months on, and I am sure it will for along time yet...

First job after Christmas is to try to get him to learn to live without me constantly being there. I just don't have the energy for it anymore; yet what they did at the hospital meant I still have no choice but to look after him. I love him and I couldn't leave him in the care of the local authority; at the rate it took them to get him into a bed, that extremely rare piece of bedroom furniture that took nineteen hours in total to find, but looking after him can sometimes be hard work.

This last round of the 'battle of the illness' had finished me off, but I think it could have been so different. If he had got the right help in the first place, the local Primary Care Trust have worn me out, not Rex.

Anyway, back to the story, he is in Liverpool and I am just about to go to bed, it was the first bank holiday in May 2006 and I was bloomin glad to see the back of it. I wasn't due back in work till Friday, my GP had signed me off again due to the fact that I was truly exhausted. I hoped he would be back in a local hospital by then and I would easily be able to work around that. If I have ever been exhausted it was that day but I still couldn't sleep.

Waterloo

It was after a minimal amount of sleep and much tossing and turning that Lisa and I set of for the hospital the next day. It was the beginning of May and a lovely bright and sunny day but I was worried; I know how badly he reacts to anything slightly traumatic; like having to pay his own credit card bill or shopping for food, or even spending longer than a few hours by himself could upset him. I could only imagine how he had coped with this little lot.

I knew what state he was in when I left him at our local hospital; but that was not going to be the same man I would be seeing now. His screams during his restraint were still echoing in my ears. I knew what he had been through this weekend would quite likely have pushed him over the edge on a normal day, never mind with an unstable mind like his had been when I left him. It's like comparing a fracture to a break in bone; you might get away with walking around with a fracture for a day or two but with a break you need it looking at straight away.

We pulled into the hospital car park an hour and twenty minutes later. The receptionist booked us in and we sat and waited. It was a clean, open hospital and the patients walking around all looked happy enough. The staff seemed to appear happy and relaxed. Watching them laughing and relaxed with patients took me back to my days at a hospital called the Retreat; that's exactly what that place had been, the nicest place I will ever work. Quite likely a very nice place for its patients and this place felt just the same.

Gordon came through the door and introduced himself. I was relieved to see his happy, smiling, reassuring face. Gordon believed that Rex had been quite traumatised on arrival; he had been very loud and aggressive but had calmed down over night. He had continually asked for me, Fred and Dave.

Gordon took us through to the ward; Rex's face was a picture. He started hugging and kissing me like he hadn't seem me for years; I must admit it felt a lifetime to me since I had last seen him. I can only

121

imagine what it must have been like for him, he had been locked up in that cell. At least I had been at home in my hours of distress.

He spotted the bag. He knew I would have bought his clothes. He stood there wearing some holey joggers, a ripped t-shirt and black pumps. We smiled at each other; I could tell what he was thinking he would need to get changed.

He has always been particular about his appearance; I think it comes from the army training. Without warning he whipped off the horrible clothes and found something more suitable from his own bag.

Lisa and I started laughing as we both turned our backs; though I'm not sure why I did, I had seen it all before! He didn't always whip his clothes off in front of an audience; although it has been known, and he isn't a prude. Years of shared showers and bathroom facilities had made him open about his nakedness.

It didn't take long for him to spot the diet coke either, his favourite tipple since giving up the booze. Again he appeared to be dying of thirst, but here there was limitless tea, water and other drinks, so I felt sure he would be ok. He was still dehydrated but he had only been here for less than twenty four hours; I knew he was going to be looked after.

We spent a good few hours at the hospital, the staff making us tea and talking to us, finding out as much as they could about Rex. They seemed genuinely interested in him as a person. Three staff members were on duty to look after him, it was clear that our hospital had sent him with a big health warning; with a dangerous man like Rex they weren't taking any chances.

This was hysterical; he is many things but dangerous isn't really one of them. I still struggled to work out where it came from; he had only spent two and a half hours observations in a ward full of broken furniture; broken before Rex went to stay I may just point out.

Steve one of the carers there said that they had been surprised by him as they had been lead to believe he was going to be big trouble, that they had not found him too much of a problem.

I know he was making a lot of noise, shouting and being a little inappropriate but he seemed to respond well to the staff. They managed to keep him distracted and on an even keel.

I told the staff at Waterloo the same as I told our local hospital; that is him all over, loud and gobby but not violent or dangerous, he has never been that.

The staff; all male on the first ward, were fantastic. Steve and Dave I remember from the first day. They were very friendly and extremely reassuring. As we left, a little guy called Dexter chased us up the corridor; desperate not to miss us he introduced himself as Rex's key worker. Assigned to make sure everything was in place for Rex during his stay for assessment in their hospital.
He wanted to know everything about Rex; what he liked, his dislikes, favourite foods, sports, football team, colour and anything else that he could think of asking about.

I told him everything I could think of. I asked what sort of activities and things they would do with him whilst he was here. I knew they wouldn't be starting any formal treatments like psychotherapy or any major medication unless it was needed; he was here for assessment but that didn't mean he had to be just locked up.
I ended up talking with Dexter for about an hour. He reassured us he would make sure Rex was well looked after and supported. Once again, I was thankful for his open and friendly approach. I could feel the commitment to caring for patients emitting from all the staff, even the receptionist cared.

I explained to Dexter I was worried Rex was getting upset when I left. Realising he may have got upset about me leaving our local hospital caused me concern. I had seen this a lot when people don't understand why they have to be locked up to get the treatment they need. It is quite common. I think "who does like being in hospital?" trying to ensure that all angles were covered; I knew I couldn't take any more stress at this stage.

Again I was given assurances they would look after him. They also confirmed they expect this; keeping ill people locked up is a tricky business. They are still patients with an illness and do have Human Rights. The use of the mental health act is clearly defined "to protect" people; not to lock them away like prisoners. Dexter promised to spend time with him once I had left; he pointed out there was a phone on the ward, available for me to contact him once I got home for reassurance; on both sides.

As we drove away from the hospital I was extremely relieved; they seemed to be looking after him well. I told them everything I could to help them understand him. The information I shared with Gordon about Rex's life long commitment to taking the mick out of scousers was beginning to show itself; he had already been making jokes; talking in his phoney accent, much to Gordon's hilarity - as I said Gordon is Scottish and found it all extremely funny.

The first few days were hard. It was clear he had had a mental breakdown but medically how and why it had happened was still largely unanswered.

Rex's doctor at this hospital believed he did have sunstroke, and was severely dehydrated upon his arrival. This can of course contribute to a person's mental well being. He also tested positive for small traces of cannabis.
I know he had smoked a joint with someone whilst he was away, so this didn't shock or cause me much concern for reasons I have mentioned before.
We also know he was attacked by a gang of thugs trying to stop them from attacking an old bloke; a substantial head injury was apparent.

I think it was the combination of everything that made him breakdown; stuck in reverse as me and Lisa had agreed; thinking back to the Coldplay song he'd driven me mad with the two days he was at home.

I just continued to pray he could get the help he deserved; they seemed to be providing it.

They did a series of tests over the first week. His moods remained up and down; with some small periods of confusion. But the staff felt he was making steady progress calming down; slowing himself down so his brain was able to start to function "normally" again.

They also said he was very easy to distract and manage; if he did start getting anxious about things they would take him for a walk or play table tennis; maybe a game of pool, anything that would make his days more productive. The staff always had funny stories to tell when I rang or visited the ward.

They started taking him to a local café for his breakfast; as well as out to local shops. He was keeping them all in sweets and cakes from the bakery; taking him to the shop meant the staff would get to choose the goodies for the rest of the ward. To be honest, I think this was some of the best support I have ever seen.

I went in to see him every other day. Although it was a nice, friendly place to visit, I knew Rex would be unsettled when I left. That is another sore point as I didn't think that it was just because he was in hospital; I think that had started a long while back and he had to learn to cope without me.

You see over the years he has left me many times to go to war; away on exercises, holidays, weekends away but over the last years he had become too dependent on me; choosing to stay away from people so they couldn't guess how unwell he had become. This had kept him at home most of the time on evenings and weekends, so every time I have gone out even to work he needed constant reassurance I was coming back. He had developed a problem with me leaving him that was slowly pushing me away.

Maybe that had occurred because in his mad anxious periods since he'd left the army he had done plenty of things that would have made me not come back.

In the last few years this has lead to me not leaving him too much and when I did go out I would try cutting down on the time I spent with friends and family. I started to realise that had probably contributed to this problem now, he obviously couldn't cope without me; he had become completely dependant and I took some responsibility for that. Rex and I spoke about how this had happened during my visits with him; he really wanted to sort it out. He constantly told me he didn't want me to look after him; he wanted me to be his wife like I used to be.

This had only developed over the last three years. Before that we'd been one of those couples who often spent time apart, what with his army commitments and girly holidays, separation had never been a problem; in fact it contributed to keeping the relationship "new". After twenty years together I had to be honest; I told him I would help him as much as I could but he would have to sort out his own life.

He had to realise he was in charge of it, not his illness, or me or anything else. Rex was responsible for Rex no more being dependant.

The hospital was managing the situation well. Again I wondered if this had been part of the problem at our local hospital; I ran over in my head, if I could have prevented the police situation… I didn't blame myself; our local hospital staff made the choice to "treat" him like they had without consulting me; that is why the police had become involved.

I left him to be cared for; they decided to lock him in a police cell.

The first of two incidents that caused a problem at Waterloo was when he decided to be racist. I haven't known him be racist before; he is very confused about racism and asylum like half the rest of the population. I couldn't say his mouth is politically correct; like many other people he sometimes slips up with his descriptions of people but his thoughts about it are not extreme.

Within the first few days he had decided that he would have a go at the nurses, quite a few of them were black that day. During one of his early manic periods he started calling the black staff racist names. I have seen this behaviour in him before too.

Let me explain. In the past I have been called a lazy cow on days when I have just finished a ten or twelve hour slog at work. I could be called fat for the very first time in my life (he has never called me fat); very strange when you consider that I have shrunk by three and a half stone on a stress based diet in recent years!
The thing about being manic is your brains going haywire; nothing and no-one is safe from your nasty thoughts; they trip freely into words from your mouth.

How many times do "non mad" people apologise for things they say; things that slip out? The really good ones can make you want to sew up your own mouth; or hope for the floor to swallow you whole. It's a trait that is present in many mere mortals; being manic just makes it worse.

Having learnt over the years to block out the insults; the ones which can be chucked at you when you live with or work with interesting people who happen to be mad. You learn to ignore most of it. Having done both I had perfected it, and that had lead to the 'lazy cow' remarks. The more I learnt to ignore Rex's behaviour the worse the insults got, to the point they became quite funny.

I think when he started calling the staff names they had probably tried to ignore him; it is unfortunate but you do get used to being sworn at in these environments.
In the past, when he wanted a response from me when I was probably too tired and exhausted to argue with him anymore; mostly over nothing, other than how unhappy he was with everything, he would up the game by saying outrageous things that would get my attention...
I think that's what happened that day; luckily it passed quite quickly, just a few hours one morning.
I think using derogatory language was probably quite liberating for Rex. I have hardly ever seen him be rude to anyone other than in moments of madness; outside of our close family it would be unheard of.

Like I keep saying he was completely compliant with any treatment or therapy that was offered; on this day he agreed to take medication to calm himself down. Within hours he apologised. He could immediately recognise he had upset people after this incident; the hospital staff spoke to him a lot about recognising when he was starting to feel anxious or stressed and out of control, and then started showing him how to cope and deal with it as a result of what happened that day.

The second incident happened about ten days or so into his stay at Waterloo. I had been for a visit and as usual I said I would ring when I got home. I tried and tried to get through on the phone but I couldn't; so I rang the office.

I spoke to a night nurse; he said the phone had been taken out of the ward because one of the patients had been messing about with it. He said he would go and check and make sure the phone was on the ward. I continued to try and call and still couldn't get hold of Rex; so I rang back and this time the nurse said it was too late for the phone to be plugged in so I would have to speak to him the next day.

I accepted this, knowing that on a night shift there were less staff to sort things out; they had just got side tracked but I did worry that I hadn't spoken to him either. I knew how anxious he could get about my whereabouts but they were looking after him well so I didn't worry too much.

The next morning my mobile started ringing. I saw it was the ward phone and felt relieved; I knew he would be worried. However, on answering, Rex started ranting down the phone about being restrained and pushed over. I wondered what had happened. He said it was over using the phone.

I rang the hospital staff straight back to find out what had happened. Gordon chuckled as he explained that they had to restrain him the previous night; he had apparently hatched a plan and tried to escape. Rex had been proud of the fact that his plan had worked; he had got onto the street. He managed to send staff off on legitimate tasks having taken the closest seat to the exit, sneakily putting his trainers out of his bedroom window in preparation for a quick dash out of the fire door.

I am sure Gordon mentioned the fact that they were going to be calling him 'Houdini' from now on! It wasn't the best situation for Rex but they had to restrain him; it was the law, he was being detained under a section.

He had conveniently forgotten to tell me all of this during our conversation earlier; that it was the phone in the street that he had tried to use!

I was quite happy that morning; a smile broke onto my face and turned up the corners of my mouth for the first time in weeks. Despite the fact that he had been restrained, plotting his escape to use the pay phone down the street and remembering my mobile number; a number he has rang constantly no less than a thousand times a year for the last seven years. Strangely, up to this point he had either forgotten the number, or chosen not to ring it since his breakdown. I thought this was a good sign, that his memory was returning in some form and his thoughts were much clearer; he was now putting ideas and thoughts together, his brain was stabilising…

The restraint had only happened because he didn't want to be locked up; being told when he can and can't talk to his wife. Why couldn't he call me for reassurance? In some ways I would agree with him one hundred percent; he hadn't behaved like he needed locking up until I left him at our local hospital; witnessed only by the staff; supposedly causing enough palaver to warrant removal to a police cell and detention under the act. Waterloo was just using a few rules to be fair to all patients; they were trying to be fair by not giving Rex favours with the phone; he just couldn't see it because he was anxious about my whereabouts.

The staff at Waterloo admitted they had witnessed a minority of behaviour that overly concerned them since his arrival; some of that could have been caused by his time spent in a cell rather than his illness. Let's not forget he now realised how long he had been ill for; that was a massive step for him in his recovery process.

I couldn't condemn the hospital for it either. I knew and understood that wards like Waterloo had to have some rules and regulations; they were responsible for keeping him locked up. They were assessing him and abiding by the law as they were being paid to do by our local authority; they were the ones using the section. I totally understood what had happened the night before; in the hospitals where I have worked we have dealt with similar situations; they had been busy and he had got stressed because he couldn't speak to me; that was all. Rex had no problem asking staff for help or accepting it, no problem with taking the medication he was offered, it was just the being locked up part that he had a problem with.

When I spoke to Rex later that day he confirmed he was going to the phone box because they wouldn't let him use the phone. He said he would have gone back to the hospital; he only had enough change to use the phone, and he was a hundred and twenty miles from home. It was a well planned escape; three people were watching him, he sent one to get him cigarettes from the office, the next to get him a cup of tea and then, whilst the third was distracted watching the news, he put his finger through the fire escape buzzer and walked out of the fire exit.

Dave was proud that his dad had tried to escape; it was the sort of thing we would expect from Rex; planning to walk out of a door, not fighting his way through the staff, as had been suggested by our local hospital labelling him violent and aggressive.

Dave saw this as a sign his dad was getting better. For years we had been supporting him; assisting him during visits to the doctors. But the problems with the crap consultant at the local hospital had always put him off asking for help. Now he had to accept that he needed it for his illness, and was happy to take it.

Big Brother was starting on the TV. It was all over the papers and on the TV every night. Ever since the first series I have been hooked; I love watching peoples' behaviour; why we do what we do...I am one of those saddos that likes it even more now they are doing experiments on the human guinea pigs... Fantastic!

For the last seven years, Rex has moaned for thirteen weeks of each; every night having to watch it. By week three or four he is as hooked as me, but he still moans.

It was the start of summer; the BB hype was everywhere. One day, when I went to visit, he asked if I had put him in the Big Brother house. He was quite serious. We turned it into a joke with the staff, we started laughing and joking but by the end of the day Rex had convinced all the patients that they were in Big Brother!

Pointing out all the fire alarms and lights in the ceilings as cameras; it was truly bonkers but he was getting better and was making everyone laugh.

In some ways I hadn't seen him this chilled out in years. It was cool. Rex, fancying himself as a singer was walking round singing Gnarls Barkley's 'Crazy'; it was playing on every radio station; the words were playing in my head too...

Once a week they would do ward round. All of the team involved in his care attended. I was always invited to go; they would check on his progress and listen to him explaining how he felt. They would then reveal the plans concerning Rex for the following week.

Like I said, they were quickly taking him off the ward and getting him out to the shops, and playing football in the sun. Rex was happily showing of his gymnastic skills; cart-wheeling through the garden as the country and the staff (mostly male) of Waterloo was warming up for the World Cup.

It seemed that he was not a threat to himself or anyone else; he is a full on bloke with an illness. But as I said all along, he isn't violent or aggressive. I was relieved that this hospital seemed to have discovered that. They weren't giving him medication, except for sleeping tablets and a few chill pills on occasions when he had felt stressed.

Not many other people have witnessed him suffering with his illness; I was pleased that we were getting more opinions and ideas for treatment from the staff at the hospital. The staff and clinical team were happy that he didn't need sectioning; as long as our local hospital started his treatment.

A section two only lasts for 28 days and that time was passing fast.

Rex did ask me why he had been locked up in a cell that turned into a tomb. He knew it was a police cell; he remembered only bits of it. He thought it was a tomb and that he was surrounded by beetles, spiders, snakes and other creepy crawlies. He had been so dehydrated that he was hallucinating; with his mental health I am sure it was torture. The only answer I could give him was that I didn't know why he had been locked up, and that I would try to look after him to make sure it didn't happen again.

He had two massive sores on his wrists from the hand cuffs they had used to transport him in. They were taking a long time to heal and he was clearly traumatised by it all. But we could talk about it and the staff at the hospital was extremely supportive to us both.

On the days in between visiting I had been in contact with our own local hospital; to let them know what they were saying about Rex at Waterloo. They seemed to expect that he would leave the hospital before the end of his section as he was doing so well. Since the early incident with the black staff there had been nothing to warrant keeping him locked up.

Nobody from our local area had been to assess him. I told the matron several times that he was coming home and that he needed treatment. That's what Waterloo's assessment of him had been , and on a section two they had only asked, and paid, for a 28 day long assessment.

The matron kept insisting that they needed to assess him. I asked when they would assess him because he was being discharged from his section within a week. She didn't seem interested. When I pointed out they were paying for an assessment she got stroppy with me; I only asked why they were paying so much for something, then insisting that they do it again themselves; it just seemed extremely strange.

My poor husband, who they had failed to look after, was going to be failed again. I tried to explain to the matron that he didn't have to be in hospital, they could put teams to support him in the community; he would of course be coming back to stay at my house when he was discharged...

I spoke to a woman who dealt with complaints several times; resulting in me putting in a complaint regarding the treatment, or rather the lack of treatment, they were giving to Rex.

I didn't want to complain; I wanted to get him home and get him well. But I hoped it might flag his case to the managers; it might get hurried along.

I know the government have told the NHS to prioritise treatment for PTSD suffers from the Armed Forces; serving Queen and Country must have some perks... Surely?

Restraint and detention for twenty hours was neither dignified nor respectful; I still couldn't understand how it had got as far as the police being involved; I thought they might want to put it right, but they obviously didn't think they had got it wrong.

They had told me that first night it would be short term; once a bed became available; it had been nearly a month.

Paying all that money for an assessment, and then denying him the treatment he now needs, taking absolutely no responsibility being in charge of his care; friends started using the word negligent to describe the situation; I must say it was starting to feel like it to me.

Even though a team of professional, respectable doctors and therapists who had looked after him well for nearly a month were saying he wasn't mad enough to be locked up under a Section of the Mental Health Act, but he was mad enough to need treatment, the local hospital still didn't listen.

All I could do was keep ringing in between visits, speaking to the hospital matron. Trying to get some support in place for his return home, the matron's attitude was disgusting; never mind the customer being right she called the customer a liar on several occasions...

At the same time I was speaking to the lovely woman in the complaints department, but the two just didn't match. One said one thing; the other said something different. To be honest neither did anything; this was the problem; action was needed, not pig-headed hospital managers trying to be clever.

I had spent nearly £1,500 going back and forth to Liverpool on petrol and stuff, but they didn't care; I was too ill with stress and exhaustion to go to work. My family life was devastated and all because our local health authority didn't seem to be able to look after a sick person when he needed it.

I had also spoken to various charities and voluntary agencies; SSAFA, Combat Stress and the British Legion, to try and get support for my husband but it didn't seem right to have to rely on charity for his health care; someone would have to help. I was exhausted and stressed before this lot started.

I have been coping with all this by myself for years, this was just the icing on the cake; someone had to help.

I did get help from the charities, and my local volunteer for Combat Stress gave me some ideas where we might be able to get treatment for Rex. He also confirmed that Rex wasn't the only veteran in our area being treated like this by the local health authority.

I also contacted the Veterans Agency for the purpose of applying for a pension for him; he must be entitled to something; he has lost his job because of his illness. In all honesty, sometimes it does still amaze me how long he continued to work for.

Luckily we have a well respected private hospital offering treatment for PTSD for a price in our local area. I had worked there in the past and felt sure that they would help if they could. It was the only old hospital I had ever been in that makes you feel happy.

A real retreat for ill people; you can tell they look after people well by the way the patients mostly always smile!

My frustration with the local authority continued; I wrote in and complained; spoke to various people. I even went to see my own GP. I was still off work with exhaustion and stress but he couldn't help, it was out of his hands.

In the end, a couple of days before they knew they were going to discharge Rex, the consultant at Waterloo spoke to our local consultant and was assured that Rex would be picked up by mental health services in our local area as soon as they let him leave.

The attitude of the Matron at our local hospital was terrible; I think she didn't like me because I asked the right questions. She was very rude and abrupt; even hinted that I was as mad as my husband.

I think she was driving me mad; all I wanted was some local treatment for a sick man...to ease the pressure on me and my family; all she wanted to do was make excuses for not being able to provide it.

Fighting them to try and get something in place to look after him once we got home on top of a two hundred and twenty mile round trip every other day to see my sick husband; the trauma they had caused us both on the day, they took him to the police station, the fact this had been going on for nearly a month whilst my son was in the middle of his final exams, made me want to say "excuse me matron for being a little stressed but as mad as my husband is this was an insult for one reason alone". The fact that at this precise moment in time I didn't have the luxury of allowing myself a breakdown, just a break would do.

Of course, we have to remember that breakdowns can vary in degrees; sometimes you run out of petrol, sometimes it's the fan belt; easily fixed problems that would see you quickly on your way. On another day your engine might blow up, causing longer termed problems, so who was she to making assumptions about how mad my husband or I were?

After three weeks of assessments and tests for everything known to man; they were letting him come home. He clearly had a manic episode after years of suffering from several serious symptoms of PTSD bought on by "whatever".

I was pretty sure they were going to let him come home after ward round the next day; he was well enough to be in the community. They had seen no evidence that suggested he should be kept locked up. As I mentioned, making the decision to use a section to detain someone for assessment or treatment should not be done lightly.

Without careful monitoring it can quickly become like a prison sentence. Waterloo, being committed to upholding patients rights certainly didn't want to detain people under the act for any longer than necessary; after the careful and thorough assessment they had done, they deemed it unnecessary.

It was clear in Rex's case that the detention was causing more issues than his mental health; he was also very aware of the distance I had to travel to visit, and the cost.

Obviously he had no money coming in at all at this stage, and had actually been spending on credit cards before coming into hospital. I was trying to keep up with everything; my mortgage, bills and travel costs, and on top of all that all of his daily living expenses; they can be high when you insist on buying everyone cakes everyday.

I spoke to the matron of our local hospital again; it was clear they were aware of my complaints, yet the day before his return home she had no offer of support for us.

By this time I had even contacted my local MP. His kind assistant told me to go back to the charity Combat Stress to get support from over stretched volunteers, rather than an MP asking the local hospital why they are so crap.

When I told the matron they were going to let him home the next day she laughed and said she didn't think so. I trusted the staff at Waterloo;

when they said they had spoken to the consultant he had obviously forgotten to tell the matron. I assured her that this was the information I had been given and that she could check these facts with Waterloo if she wanted.

I don't think she bothered.

They had been quick to lock him up in the most outrageous way possible, they had assured me that they would move him nearer to home as soon as possible but the fact is they had done nothing since having him taken to the police station. They had done nothing except lock him up.

It was all starting to get me down. I don't normally do self pity but at this stage it started to creep in. We are a cool little family of three; good and kind. Rex and I have paid our taxes, we have always worked and never used the NHS for much, but here I was, having to beg for help for my sick husband; it was hard to cope.

My life has always been difficult but whose hasn't? Life is hard; I have always managed to stay on top of stuff but the anxiety caused by having a sick husband who needed basic psychological input, a couple of visits from a nurse each week, maybe a little medication, some support was like getting blood from a stone; and it felt like it could be my downfall. Banging your head against a brick wall to get basic treatment for someone who so needs and deserves it could drive you mad. In fact, for a while I think it did.

The same frustration I am sure felt by the increasing number of sick people we see on the news; having to fight for a cancer drug or some such life saving treatment.

Having to fight battles when you need care should not be acceptable for anyone but it does seem mental health is the poorest relative of the NHS. Offering no care or provision for treatment at all must be negligent.

Although I have worked in Mental Health for a long time I have always steered clear of working for the NHS. They don't ever seem to regard improving Mental Health services as a priority; I think this has something to do with the fact they can blame 90% of their failure and complaints in this department on the client group. They are mad after all, if they say there is something wrong with their treatment; it is easy for staff to say that the complaints are part of their illness. The other thing they do a lot is blame substance abuse; quite a lot of people I have come across self medicate for stress, depression, anxiety; with drink or drugs, and for really ill people it can end up as both…

The health authorities classify those patients as 'drug addicts' rather than people with mental health problems. What comes first the illness or the "self" medicating? As far as I am concerned this is as complex a conundrum as the chicken and egg scenario.

Our local Primary Care Trust website shows statistics that indicate a clear decline in the provision of mental health services over the last years.

In explaining why things go wrong with patient care I have seen the following in people's notes. Recording things like patients wanting to talk as demanding behaviour, being depressed and lying on your bed can become refusing to interact with services. No one actually seems to have time to listen to, or look at, the reality of the situation for these people; so the staff have their backs covered and the hospitals can turn their own symptoms against the patient in recording "outcomes" for patients. They blame the patients for the revolving door situation; people get in trying to deal with poor mental health; often in and out of hospital like a merry go round ride.

This is instead of admitting what the real problems are, such as no services being available or not enough staff to cover the beds that they have.

Anyway, by the end of the day I had got no further forward with getting some help in place so I had booked an appointment with our GP for Thursday; that way if anything is going wrong I'd have his backup. I also spoke to him about getting in touch with the Mental Health Team. My GP assured me this would be done by the hospital.

I wasn't so sure, I knew how much I had tried to get them to put something in place, to look after him but they weren't having any of it. I really didn't believe they would help but I had to trust someone here and my GP was the best option.

I spent the evening with Dave. It was a Monday night; we went out to the local Chinese and spent some quality time together.
I knew it was going to be hard work looking after Rex; I needed to make sure we were both ready for it.
Dave was still doing his GCSE'S and the stress was starting to take its toll. Dave had only seen his dad once in the past three weeks. I had taken him over one Saturday with Fred and our friend Lisa. The hospital had made it a nice day; they gave us a family room and made us welcome with tea and stuff. Lisa and Dave went round to the local bakery and bought a big picnic lunch, it was a cool day but I had decided that he needed to concentrate on his exams so I'd kept him away, they spoke on the phone daily but I needed to make sure he was ready for the home coming tomorrow.

They hadn't confirmed it but I knew they would let him go; I knew in my heart he could have been nursed better in the beginning and the need to lock him up, and label him as a dangerous mad man avoided. But that's life and for now he had to depend on someone; that someone was to be Dave and I again.
When they let him leave the hospital tomorrow I knew I had to bring him home and look after him.

I had arranged visits from the veterans' agency and combat stress to try and line up support and money.
I love him a lot, but at this stage I didn't have any money left and not much energy to support myself let alone him as well, but I had to keep going.

As I drove out to Liverpool for the last time I felt a little sad. They had been kind and supportive, not only of Rex but of me and my family too. I knew that level of care was not available to everyone everywhere but I was pleased that they had been able to help him the way they had.

I pulled into the hospital; all of the staff was rooting for Rex! I think they truly thought he needed to be closer to his family to get better. I don't think they wanted rid of him; he had kept most of the hospital supplied with cakes, sweets and any other goodies he could get his hands on whilst out on his daily trips to the shops, as well as using them to bribe the younger lads on the ward to tidy themselves, and their rooms. He even got blokes doing stuff the fantastic staff couldn't with the aid of his powers of persuasion, Mars bars, fags......

We met with all of the staff involved in his assessment; they all said the same - he could go home but needed to get treatment as soon as was possible. They knew that Rex was keen to have some therapy to help him cope; he had ran from his illness for years but they had achieved helping him come to terms with it and helped him learn that you can manage it if you knew how to.

I told them about the support from various charities and they had confirmed talking to our local hospital again; it was a relief when they said I could take him home. His mind was still wobbly but he needed to be near his family.
It was a shame that our local hospital hadn't assessed him but I didn't feel at any risk, or worried in anyway, so we set off for home.
I felt sure once I had him home the matron would have to listen to me, and provide some level of care for Rex.

During the drive home he was very excited about little luxuries; like sleeping in his own bed, drinking tea from his own teapot, chilling out. It can be full on in psychiatric hospitals when you have only brief periods of madness. It means in your sane minutes you still have to live with other people are very poorly.
This had been the case with Rex; being in hospital had taken its toll on him. He had got very upset by stories of people locked up under section for years, with no one to look after them or fight for their

rights; they had no hope of beating a poor mental health system that has people locked up for being mad instead of treating them.

Many people can't get out of hospital because there simply aren't enough places for them to live or get support in the community; in some cases they are kept hundreds of miles from home for years.

The ones Rex met in that hospital didn't moan about Waterloo; most of them having been in the system for sometime knew it was probably the best care on offer; for people that are sectioned they had places to compare it to, Rex didn't.

It did upset Rex though; he seemed to appreciate the stuff I had been telling him for years, about how lucky we are to have good friends and family to look after us.

He had felt like the whole world has been against him for the last few years, sometimes so depressed he could stay in his dressing gown and not leave the house for days. In between his anxiety he would have little manic episodes. He would cry over silly things; it had been heartbreaking to watch... Now he saw what a problem this had been, and even how it had got to breaking point for us both.

I think Rex's life has been a little sheltered; no one in the army had drug addictions, or mental health issues, or drink problems. Or at least they didn't talk about it openly, as I have mentioned before alcoholism was acceptable.

I know it was definitely there. Many years before, at the age of twenty, we had Dave; I had given birth in a military hospital in Germany. A few of Rex's mates were in hospital at the same time on what was called P wing.

This was a ward for soldiers who needed help with problems with drink. This was 1989 and young lads of 20 and younger were being dried out, like I said, the upside was I always had plenty of visitors in the weeks I spent cooped up in hospital.

He has never paid bills or looked after himself; none of our friends or family have any major problems, a few medium-sized but not massive; he hadn't seen this sort of stuff before; real people with problems beyond belief. He has been lucky really; now he seemed to be starting to realise it.

I believe you make your own luck and once you start having bad luck you have to change your ways by yourself in order to change it.

Most people in hospital didn't have much contact with their families; this is not surprising when you see what families have to go through to try and get treatment for these people. It is an extreme battle and this is happening all the time to lots of families. Families must run out of energy trying to fight the system, instead of using that energy to support their relative or friend. I had experienced it first hand, and it wasn't nice.

Running out of money to visit would have been a problem if I didn't have my fence and fire money to spend...

Care in the community is a joke; people can't get out of the system because they are just a little bit too ill to cope by themselves, but there is no support available, so they keep people locked up because the right support isn't there. If they become informal patients they will leave and have no support then go into crisis again; it is a vicious, frustrating circle to get stuck in for thousands of people.

Gordon told me to ring if there were any problems, Dexter ran up the corridor, there was much hugging in between well wishes from everyone; staff and patients, everyone. One laughed as Rex called Dexter, Denzil for the last time. Twenty days of someone calling you by something other than your real name would wind up a saint but Dexter had been ace... As I drove towards home with Rex looking up into the sky on this sunny day saw a little cloud drifting past. I hoped they'd have to support him once I got him home... He still definitely needed treatment.

Home

We arrived home at teatime; it was a joy to watch as he took Dave in a big bear hug, the two of them smiling at each other, hugging and kissing like long lost friends.

Dave immediately said he saw a big change in Rex; it had been three weeks since he last saw him. For the first time ever Rex was openly talking about what was wrong with him and he knew he needed treatment. He also seemed to relax, as soon as he knew he was home and safe again.

This was all alien to us, the man who had gone abroad a few months earlier had been a loud, verbally aggressive prat with a mental health problem that, on some levels he didn't believe he had. He left me all those times because he said his life was crap, it had been crap because he was ill, not because his life was really crap. Now he realised that.

This man was a calm, lovely man with an illness that was apparent but not intimidating like it had been before. He was still quite hyper, I think the excitement of being home was overwhelming for him. He wanted to constantly touch me and Dave to make sure we were still near.

The evening passed without much hassle. It was hard to keep up with him, he had loads of people to talk to whilst he was in hospital, and he was burning my ears out in the nicest way possible, he kept saying how sorry he was for the last few years and how much he loved me and Dave; how much he appreciated our support and love. It was the only true, constant, thing in his life and for the first time in at least three years he seemed to really appreciate that fact.

We had been through a lot together, but this gave us hope that all would be well for our little family.

He just needed the right treatment; our GP had agreed to refer him to our local private hospital, all I had to do was find the two grand to pay for it. I was determined he would get the right help, so not finding the money was not an option.

I clearly couldn't trust the National Health Service to provide anything; unfortunately though that meant that I was still responsible for looking after him and I'd signed up to be his wife, not his carer.

They had put him on sleeping tablets whilst he was in hospital so he took it at 10 O'clock; we went to bed. It had been a really long day and we were all ready for bed. He was out like a light. I lay next to him, watching him sleep. I had still been having trouble sleeping myself ; what with all the travel back and forth to Liverpool, I felt as tired as a tired thing, but still I couldn't sleep. I lay for ages watching him sleep. To be honest I was crying; it made me so sad to see him so vulnerable, my brave soldier had gone; now he was going to need a lot of help to get over this.

I was still having the nightmare, still hearing him screaming as the police restrained him. This was the first night I had been able to comfort him since that had happened. He has very nasty scars on his wrists that he rubbed constantly from the handcuffs, and every time I looked at them I could see it flash in my mind.
I lay next to him crying; he had been a good husband to me over the years, before he got ill I had not often gone without, he spoilt me. He had loved and protected me and now it was my turn to look after him. I was sure it would be much easier than it had been before he wanted treatment and the end was in sight, Thursday. Seeing the GP would see the referral for the private treatment complete and then it was all moving in the right direction.

My heart broke though as I looked into his face whilst he slept, thinking of the journey we had been on to get to this point, I had to put the police incident out of my mind, but I couldn't.

But he was home safe and all I had to do was watch over him till the mental health services came. I hoped it would be by the weekend. The way they had him down I would have expected them to believe he was a high risk to the public, thus giving him some sort of priority. I had spoken directly to the community mental health team the day before they said they should get a referral from the consultant. I was trying not to get stressed with it all; over the last month I had learnt to expect nothing from them; why get stressed about it, expect nothing, so anything you get is a bonus.

Waterloo had confirmed a conversation with our local consultant Dr Nopal, and we knew that he was fully aware of Rex's condition; he had met him a couple of times before.

Wednesday morning dawned and we needed to go sort out his money and stuff at the bank. I drove us into town and walked around the shops, stopping to have some breakfast in a small café.

Later in the day we were expecting a visit from the Veterans Agency to help fill in some pension forms; if Rex was suffering from PTSD then he would be entitled to a pension, and this stage any little would help. I had to pay the bills whether he was there or not, so he could live rent free, but he had to cover his own living costs. He had been earning well over 20 grand a year and now he had no income, and overdrafts, credit card bills and loan payments to make...

I was moving money around between our accounts to try and stop bank charges. I hoped she would be able to sort it out for him as the money problems were obviously a big worry for him. He has earned good money for years, he had outgoings to match. They still needed to be paid and I could only help in the short term.

She arrived and bought along another woman who lives not far from us who also suffers from PTSD. I hoped that they could support each other a bit. I had always worried that I couldn't understand what he'd been through at war, but if he could talk to someone else it may help him to come to terms with some of the stuff.

The time flew by, and they left but they had exchanged numbers and arranged to meet up again. The claim form was done and I hoped that the army would be able to pay him a pension. It was clear the illness had been triggered by working for the Queen, and now it had nearly ruined his life. The least the government could do is relieve some of the financial stress; god knows they were not being helpful with his treatment.

We made some tea together, cooking together was something we hadn't done for years; we chatted and got on with daily stuff, a little cleaning and gardening, it wasn't too bad at all. He had been the best host that day; making all our visitors tea, and scones with piles of clotted cream. They had all appreciated it. He was on fine form, hyper, but happy would be the best description.

Thursday comes and goes again, the trip to our GP was quite funny; our GP has known us for a few years and over those years he had become the only doctor that Rex will see.

Our GP seemed happy to prescribe the sleeping tablets and maybe to look at some mood stabilising medication, but until the appointment with Dr Nopal, the consultant, took place all he could do was continue with the medication for sleeping that had been prescribed in hospital. It was all to do with the section and the responsibility of the health service to give him the right treatment; that meant waiting for the consultant.

He did as promised; to do the letter for the private treatment that we had discussed previously, and this would be completed today, again I would feel a little better; when the private hospital was a place I knew it was a good place and I knew they would be able to help.

Again the day went smoothly; he had a lot of energy still but at this stage he was calm, lovely and maybe a little tiny bit manic. He wanted to be on the go constantly; I was knackered, still trying to get over everything that happened recently. I had decided to change my GP in the same practice, I felt I needed some support that wasn't attached to Rex; whilst I adore my own GP, often my appointments could be used up talking about Rex instead of me.

So I got a new GP, she is really lovely, although most of the time I spent with her at this time in my life was spent crying my frustration and anger at my situation, filling the visits, she was one of the people who kept me sane for what was the most stressful time in my life. She was convinced I was suffering from exhaustion and stress and I think she was concerned how long I could carry on for; I hadn't slept properly for 30 nights and I was counting, every night since the nightmare had started. I had slept for a few hours at a time; fit, full, worried sleep with flash backs to what I had seen in that bloody hospital. She supported my decision not to take medication for my problems, she listened to me instead.

She just let me talk and talk, for that I am thankful and to those people whose appointments were extremely late, I apologise.

I wasn't so worried, you see many friends and family were helping and once his treatment got underway I would be able to return to work, and other people would help us to look after him.

I was thinking he would get a community psychiatric nurse, maybe a support worker, you know people to help. It had to start getting better, it couldn't get worse than it had been that was for sure.

Thursday night came, and I managed to sleep for about five hours. At last my own demons beginning to fade away. He is here, he is well, he is being looked after, and we have to get on with it; you can't stop life, pause it whilst you have a rest, it doesn't work like that does it... With still no contact from the mental health team and the bank holiday looming, I knew that they wouldn't be coming tomorrow. I started to plan in my head how we would get over the weekend, it helped me to sleep.

The only problem was I was knackered and he was hyper, you had to keep an eye on him. Still a little too poorly to be left alone for long but I believed we could get through. We had no choice.

Friday dawned; he was busy putting England flags on his car. Not that he was driving, I was taking us everywhere but I wouldn't let him put them on mine. I like England; I just don't like football...

We went out for breakfast with my sister Mandy; she was so busy laughing at him, cracking jokes, and chatting away I don't think she noticed he nicked half her breakfast. He was still quite hyper, but in real fine form. I took him to the barbers and he got himself a shave and face massage, I hoped it might chill him out and slow him down... Unfortunately it only worked whilst he was in the chair.

Lisa turned up, she had decided to drive the eighty miles between us to come and take him out for a few hours so I could get some rest.

It was just what I needed, although I am not sure why as soon as they had got back he had started acting a little strange, he seemed a bit unsettled somehow. Rex had been talking to Lisa about how stressed I was, worrying that me having to look after him was too much for me. I cuddled him as I reassured him that he would be ok, we would be ok.

I thought it was just because he'd had her rushing round and once he chilled out he'd be ok. I think she had seen every tourist attraction in our city and more...

We all ate some tea and he suddenly started getting a bit stroppy; nothing major but he had only been like that with me once since he had returned from Greece, and that was in the first week of being in hospital. He once blamed me for getting him locked up, I and the staff had put him straight and he hadn't so much as raised his voice in front of me since. When I asked him why he was being like this and he replied that he just felt a bit crap.

He was very aware that he had tired me out, and he felt guilty as he told me this, he looked like he was going to cry. I suppose I did look tired and stressed by this stage but it wasn't his fault; he had been in Liverpool getting better whilst I had been fighting the hospital and driving thousands of miles, and generally trying to hold it all together.

He then said he would like to go back to Waterloo for a bit longer; he said that there were loads of blokes there to look after him. I said we'd be ok but he said he wanted to go.

It was about 5pm on the Friday of the second bank holiday in May. I asked Rex if he wanted me to contact Waterloo and ask for advice; Rex said he thought that was the best idea, they had worked a lot on self awareness with him and I had to listen to him.

He was totally aware of his illness and he was asking for a bit more help.

I went and rang Gordon, I told him what Rex had been saying and he confirmed they could take him back in the hospital if our local health authority agreed to fund it.

I said I would ring the out of hours GP to ask advice and get back to him.

I wasn't too worried, but I had to listen to Rex he obviously recognised the signs.

I rang NHS direct, and after loads of questions and about forty minutes explaining to the GP the whole situation, he was in agreement that taking Rex back to Waterloo would be the best option. He would need to get agreement from the consultant; he said he would ring me back. It took about another forty minutes for him to call me back, but the answer was that the consultant couldn't agree funding for someone he hadn't seen.

I was devastated; they had refused to look after him all week and now he was going to have a crisis and still they can't make a decent offer. I think we have one of those super flash Crisis Intervention Teams in our area, if they had turned up this might not be happening.

Now they wanted me to take him back to A&E. I doubt there was even a psychiatric consultant in A&E unless they had recruited one in the last month; there certainly hadn't been any sign of one last time I took Rex to the hospital.

So back to square one and there was no way I was going to take him back to A&E not after the last time, would you?

Lisa hung around till about 7.30, distracting Rex whilst I made all of the calls, but I sent her home after a cup of tea. I eventually got Rex to go chill out in the bath, this had been his half hour luxury whilst in hospital and I hoped it would work now. I am not even sure what he was doing that was strange, but I knew he wasn't right and so did he.

After his long soak he got out and I settled him in front of the TV whilst I jumped in and had a bath. I could hear him bumbling about in the house; he kept shouting to me as I sat in the bath, random stuff that didn't make any sense really.

I heard him go upstairs and switch on the computer. As I got out of the bath and put on my dressing gown, I wandered up to see what he was doing. I found him looking at a website about Greek gods on the internet. To distract him for the hour or so left before his sleeping tablets, I went downstairs and put the kettle on. I hoped to convince him to take his tablet a little bit early to get him to sleep.

As he came into the lounge I told him his cuppa was ready and sat down. He started talking about gods again; a little bit like when he first came back, but more confused. I tried to distract him and talk about other things, but it wasn't working; he kept on telling me about this one particular god.

I asked him to change the subject and he slammed down his cup... I asked again what was wrong; this time he couldn't get the words out of his mouth to say; he just started shouting and swearing. Not particularly at me, just shouting, wandering round. He walked to the kitchen, I heard him in the kitchen drawer; I wondered what he was doing. He came back to the lounge, he had a knife in his hand; he turned the sofa over and he started cutting the sofa with the knife.

I stood up and left the house; I realised I was still in my dressing gown and my hair all over the place from just having uncurled it from a pony tail from the bath. My neighbours must have seen a right sight!

I knew it was calculated; you see years ago, before we were even married we were messing about in my sister's kitchen; he was pretending he was going to cut off my toes with a butter knife. I had a massive panic attack and told him about what I had seen my dad do when I was a kid, although it doesn't bother me on a daily basis I don't like to see anyone messing about with knives it is my one big phobia.

He has never jested in that way ever again, not even in the last few years when he has done some bad stuff that has freaked me out, but not the knife thing, he had known knives were too much.

Within the next thirty minutes he had completely calmed himself down he had left several messages on my answer phone.

Unfortunately though, for the half an hour that he was trying to get hold of me on the phone I was stood at the bottom of our street on the phone after ringing 999 for help. He needed an ambulance, yet it took twenty five minutes for the first police officer to turn up… All that time they kept me on the phone so I had managed to tell them how poorly he was, how he needed medical care; but they sent the police.

Eventually, at about 11pm when I got the messages left by Rex between nine and nine thirty I started to cry again, in the first voicemail he was still shouting about being a god. The next he just simply asked where I was, the next was asking me to come home. In the last one, he said he hoped I was not going to be long picking up Dave from the party he was at; he had totally calmed down.

My heart broke; I shouldn't have panicked but the month of stress caused by arguments and begging the local hospital to sort out his care, and my serious lack of sleep had made me panic for a split second.

When I left the house I ran down the street and hid in a neighbour's garden; two neighbours walked passed with their dogs but didn't bat an eyelid they just smiled and nodded like your neighbours do.
Women in the street in their nightwear must be a more regular occurrence than I thought

The emergency services came on the line and I told them what had happened; the operator told me to stay exactly where I was, but I realised that I couldn't see the house. Dave was at a party and I didn't expect him back for ages; it was only just about 9pm and this was the big leaving school party, I was sure it would probably be a little wild, he has some mad mates they would be having fun for hours.

But then you never know with teenagers, and I didn't want him walking in on his dad slicing the sofa up, or whatever he had been doing. I ran across our street and stood behind a letterbox, I could see everything from my new vantage point, but everyone could see me; my hair all over and my old dressing gown and slippers on. The post box is slap bang on a small, yet quite busy crossroad.

I'd been on the phone for about 15 minutes with the operator; giving her details. But no police had actually turned up and I was starting to get worried about Rex. He hadn't been left alone since he had come out of hospital; I thought about putting the phone down and ringing him to see how he was doing.

I knew he would be trying to ring me, wondering where I had gone. I knew him inside out. I wanted to put the phone down on the police; I knew they would be mustering an army. I knew it, in all honesty as soon as the word knife and ex-forces came out of my mouth. A guy in Newcastle had shot his whole family recently, I knew they wouldn't take any chances, telling them about his mental health didn't bring an ambulance and psychiatrist, but the knife, which knowing him he had put away by now, probably only ever getting it out as a prop to scare me and since I'd gone he didn't have any reason to have it out.. But I knew mentioning it would bring a small army of specialist police, quite likely including an armed response unit.

Eventually after about 25 minutes a police car turned up and I got in. The radio was going mad and the policeman was distracted, trying to talk to me and listen to everything going on. There are several, different radios all going off at the same time.

He said they were sorry it took so long to get there... response time laughable 25 minutes to a woman, saying her husband is cutting up her sofa, it is a good job Rex had used this time to calm himself down. He never meant any harm in the first place, or else I could have been one of those dreadful domestic violence victims who end up dead because of policing problems; too many crimes, not enough police…Or is it not enough health care that's the problem?

I knew it wasn't the officers' fault; that's just picked me up off the side of the road, so what can you say?

I am left wondering if domestic violence is a crime anymore, even these days, what if he had still been chasing me…. And not calming himself down…

My head was reeling again; this time sat in a police car in my holey old dressing gown and my hair stuck up all over the place, and a lot of police activity in the area…

My night with Max

Just then, a police van turned up and Max introduced himself. He was quite a young, tall bloke, he pulled away in the van; I started to panic again. What was happening now? I just wanted to get into my house, to check all was well. I heard him say he was taking me to the checkpoint; he drove about half a mile to an unmanned fire station.

Many police cars and people turned up asking me all sorts of questions; any guns, knives, machetes... Any history of violent crime, I told them all who he was, and what had been happening with him. It just so happened that two of the officers remembered him from the last episode. One guy had a brother in the same regiment that Rex had been in; Max had driven him over to Waterloo. He told me Rex had been calling him two names; Ben and Lewis, these are both people close to Rex and I was not surprised that he had confused this guy for them.

The whole car park was a hive of activity; more police arriving and then going again. They were asking more questions, getting me to draw pictures of the garden and house lay out. It seemed to be going on forever. I asked the police if I could call Dave; he would be leaving the party soon, it was nearly 10pm. By now I was getting very worried. To be fair the police were being cool, but there was an awful lot of them for my poor mad husband... why did I mention the bloody knife? Rex was on the phone and they couldn't get through to talk to him, they could see him walking around the lounge, but he was on the phone.

I called my friend Sharon to check she was in, my oldest, most reliable friend, her daughter was at the same party and it was likely that they would be walking home together. I wanted to check it was ok for Dave to go to their house; god knows how much longer this would take... Sharon's house phone was engaged; she is always gassing to someone so I tried her mobile, she can gas for England. Less than five minutes up the road and me and her can do an hour or more gassing and easily forget what we rung for in the first place. Her husband answered her mobile; he seemed pleased to hear from me, Mac is a gentle sort of man, always chilled out or so it seems to anyone that knows him, but I could hear a slight panic in his voice.

It made sense; Sharon was on the phone to Rex. He had rang there looking for me. They had been worried about where I was; they both knew I wouldn't be far away but my mobile had been constantly engaged so they hadn't been able to get hold of me.

Sharon ended the call with Rex so the negotiator could get through; I spoke to her briefly, the police were questioning her though, me asking what state he was in and Sharon confirmed Rex had told her he had cut the sofa, and upset me but he didn't know where I had gone; he was panicking. He had also told her he had put the knife back in the drawer, it wasn't a big knife, just the two pound fifty veggie knife from Ikea.

After the call to Sharon I got hold of Dave, I told him to go home to Sharon's; he asked why. Once again I tried to keep it light and play it down. It was only later when he had left the party and saw our street closed off by armed police vans and stuff that he realised how bad it was. He has got so used to me being in control of manic situations with his dad that he had stayed for another can of lager at the party after my call; his mate Jimmy seeing him look a little upset gave him a can of lager and a cuddle in a manly way...

Some of his mates knew what had been happening and he again had good support and with a sad face, and a free can of lager, he was surviving. He even made Sarah cross over the road thinking, that the police were going to stop them and search them for drink. It was only as they passed the top of the street that he realised it was our house all the action was at.

By now it was after 11pm and I was chatting away to poor Max like a maniac, I think his ears must have been on fire, but nerves make me talk... I have learnt in recent years this can be a bad thing sometimes, but this night my anger, frustration and lack of sleep in the last week was getting to me. I was worried for Rex. I knew all the neighbours would be watching, and I didn't know what state he was in. I still hadn't heard the messages. Sharon said he had kept drifting off into madness; but that he had been able to chat and answer her questions.

By eleven thirty it was all over; the negotiator quickly got him to come out. He isn't a fighter, I knew he wouldn't resist, but he can be very stubborn. The senior officer came over with my mobile and said I had loads of messages; it was then as me and the officer listened to them, I realised that he had calmed himself down once he realised how much he had scared me for that split second. In the time the police had taken to arrive, twenty five minutes, the first four messages had been received whilst I was on the phone to the 999 operator. There was a fifth message by the time we had finished listening to these; telling me he was just going with the police as they wanted him to go and talk, and could I sort it out.

The senior police officer wandered off; returning just a few minutes later and told us Rex had just walked out, and that he was being taken in for affray, but that already had the team on standby to assess him again.

We drove back towards the house and I could see the neighbours closing the doors as the van drove passed. I realised how much had been happening here. They are a nosey bunch; there have been a few raids at the houses down the street a few times, but not at our house.

As I tried the front door we realised they had locked us out of the house; now I am on my doorstep for ten minutes, waiting for the police to bring us a key. Some of the more brazen neighbours continued to twitch. Just as they arrive to let us in, Sharon pulled up with Dave. He had insisted on coming home as soon as he heard it had ended; she had no choice but to bring him; she knows that we three are in this together and he wanted to be with me.
There was broken glass in the hallway; it was just a broken picture frame, nothing major, it had probably fallen over when the front door had been opened or banged shut locking me out.

As we walked in, the place was pretty much as I'd left it. I walked about; Max, Sharon and Dave followed. The police had taken my new veg knife and Dave's end of year message book... You remember what it was like; he was finishing school in a few weeks, everyone was swapping messages in each others' book. Dave's had been on the side for a few days and the messages in his were coming in thick and fast; some declaring undying love for him and his whole group of friends... and other threatening to blow up the head teacher and school..... All in the name of leaving school; you remember the t-shirt signing? Everything and anything that is written down is hilarious to sixteen year old kids leaving school.

The police had thought it was Rex's mad ramblings. We got the book straight back; but my two pound fifty knife was gone forever. We do have a new one, so no need worry that we aren't eating any vegetables.

There's no major mess; although I did notice a game of footy had definitely been played in the bedroom with a large exercise ball.

The kettle went on and Max said he needed to take a statement; Dave made some tea, he is good at that; he must have made his Dad thousands trying to calm him down over the years. Sharon said she could stay, but I told her to get off, it was way past twelve.

I just wanted to give a statement and find out when they would get him to a hospital. I had told the police officers that I had contacted Waterloo and they had said they could have given him a bed back earlier; they promised to tell the approved social worker about it when she turned up to section him again; which was what we all knew would happen. An hour's crisis that could have been prevented and the local authority would lock him up again.
It would save locking him up for hours again if they just sent him straight back there to Waterloo, but I think it was probably too late for that now.
Everyone was aware how badly it had traumatised him before being locked in a police cell; I hoped he wasn't getting in that state again.

He could be quickly traumatised by the police cell situation again so close to the last time. He was fragile, and in need of treatment; that's why we had been begging for help from the hospital for the last month, since they sectioned him the first time for the assessment to be done. They had failed to treat him even though they had a very expensive assessment done...

I think again about the outrage if this was a broken leg and not head. He wasn't ill enough to be sectioned he just needed treatment, the team at Waterloo had made that clear and our own GP had not been concerned when he saw him on Thursday, but we all know fragile minds need quick treatments, not waiting lists. And now they were going to lock him up again un-frickin believable.

I sat down with a cup of tea and started to talk to Max; I told him the whole story. He looked at me; I could see he thought I must be mad to have lived like this for so long but what else I could do I wasn't sure, no one else was looking after him were they?
He started to write it all down, it took an age, poor Dave sat trying to stay awake I knew he didn't want to leave me but I sent him off to bed saying there was nothing he could do.
I realised there was nothing I could do.

I had been scared for about 1 minute, then panicked and to be honest I have been in much scarier situations with him than this, but I was exhausted and knew he needed just a little more help... 9pm on a Friday night in my lounge trying to look after my husband after weeks of begging the hospital for help it wasn't my fault this had happened. Yes I had panicked, but if they had looked after him, even just a little bit of help for us, any treatment for Rex and I was sure this could have been prevented.
My head was spinning with all these thoughts as I answered the phone to a nice police doctor; he asked me about Rex and told me they were going to section him again; that he hoped they would get him straight into hospital, he seemed concerned about Rex's welfare at least.

I started to tell Max the full story about my husband, and his illness. His crimes have only been to go a little mad, and smoke a little pot; nothing really that could have lead to his arrest. So why was he back in a cell? Even Max couldn't answer that, and I am sure the cell was needed on a Friday night for proper criminals. All those binge drinkers and yobbos that fight in the street.

An approved social worker came on the phone a little later; she was again explaining my rights as his nearest relative, and once again I made my feelings known that again I felt they were using a section, instead of providing treatment to a man that had been requesting it. I'm thinking a few days back in hospital, maybe get some medication to stabilise him and slow him down more. I am not a big believer in medication for Mental Health but sometimes people need chemical help to slow them down.

Even with his sleeping pills he had only been getting six hours a night at home.

Now they were using a section three; this could last up to six months and they can force him to take medication and other treatments against his will. It was a joke; I wasn't happy why they did not have a bed in a local ward, why do they need to detain him under a section? The social worker said that she would say I was objecting to the section, and they would keep him in the cell until they could get a higher authority to grant the section.

The conversation ended with me saying that she should do what was best for Rex; she had the responsibility for his welfare and he was vulnerable; the PCT have a duty of care to people detained in this way she needed to make decisions and look after him; especially since he had been asking for treatment.

It is about 5.30 in the morning before Max stops writing; he is getting all of the details in as these statements explaining, that they can be sometimes used as evidence or something like that.

I had to sign every bit twice; I think I was absolutely done in. I couldn't work out what Rex was wearing, and again I began to worry about him having clothes. I asked Max if he could take a bag with stuff in to the station if Rex was still there; I was assuming the police would have contacted Max if he'd been moved, not that anyone would have contacted me after the last time.

I had no idea where they would take him this time, and he would need his own stuff. It was just as Max was leaving, about six thirty, that the social worker called me back. As I asked her what had been done about moving him into a bed, she started blaming me for the delay in getting him to a hospital; saying that I had objected to the use of section 3. Max, I think heard most of the conversation this time, I explained to this woman that she and the doctor had made the decision to section him and I couldn't understand why had she not got him into a hospital; as she had decided he needed one earlier this morning...

She must have missed the module on client's rights and welfare at college; dignity and respect and all that stuff. I was sure she must have been over-tired at one stage; the social worker told me that if I didn't agree with everything she was saying about my husband being sectioned, she would have the police send him home in the next few hours.

I was worried about the treatment of my obviously sick husband again; she didn't seem to want to reassure me in anyway. She kept threatening to send him home. I told her I would welcome that and she should organise it; was it a threat? Or was he well enough to come home at that stage? Again it makes you think all sorts.

Max heard everything; I could tell by the look on his face.

In the end she said they would have to get him to a hospital as soon as possible, and that he had been sectioned... So sending him home was a threat... Again there was no reason for him to be detained in a police cell, and even less evidence on which to section him.

Max left; I lay down on the sofa, my body too wary to move. I started to sob, not crying, sobbing my little heart out. My poor man. I couldn't stop wondering what he was going through. I tried to get a little sleep between panic attacks. I knew it was going to be another long day, calls, arguments and very slow progress in getting treatment, or a bed for Rex.

This time it was to last all day. I kept badgering social services, the hospital managers and again I was unable to go to the police cell; again he is left without anyone to look after him, and once again the police are the only people that have seen him since about three am. They are the only ones that can tell me how he is doing. They were quite kind when I spoke to them, they do also keep saying they are not trained to look after ill people.

Despite using a section that states he will receive medical care, they are failing to provide it for him, and to be honest for the most part, the staff at the hospital and in social services have been rude and arrogant in dealing with me. It has been clear from the outset they were finding it difficult to deal with someone who knows and understands the system that they work within.

I refused to be fobbed off by their weak explanations for failing to look after my husband. I think a few people I spoke to came over as a little aggressive, but I felt sure this was due to constantly having to apologise for being part of a system that is failing to provide adequate care for such vulnerable people, and knowing that they probably have no power to change a single thing.

I think most people would go mad having to stand back knowing that a relative is being treated in this way, and very unfair of the NHS to expect families to go through this time and time again.

At one stage a social worker started shouting at me; asking me if I thought he liked having to keep people locked up in a cell. He calmed down; went on to explain that a high dependency unit had been planned several times to stop this sort of detention in police cells, but it's been knocked back for several reasons. Everything's more important to an NHS trust Mental Health that isn't "sexy".

So the day slowly ticks by, with all that has happened in the last month this last round is just too ridiculous for words, so I won't even try to describe how I felt. It was 6pm when they eventually found him a bed, Waterloo had not been able to offer him a bed in the end, they were too concerned about the state he would be in after prolonged detention in a cell; it had caused him massive levels of stress the last time, and they were worried about him, and me, having to go all that way again.

They had actually told me that despite the possibility of a bed locally they didn't have enough staff. It was just excuse after excuse and it was driving me mad. This time the hospital was only forty five miles away, but that was still going to be ninety miles a day on top of everything else. Within minutes I had found the hospital website and contacted them direct. Again they seemed quite friendly, but once again it was an expensive private hospital so you do expect a little bit more than you get on the NHS.

However this hospital, as I quickly found out from friends who worked around that area came with a less than good reputation.

I just kept thinking it was better than a police cell, he was there by seven forty, but this time I was still worried. They had very strict visiting times so they weren't going to let me into see him, I begged them but they said no. It would have to be the next day. I booked the first visiting slot at 2pm.

My friends and family that knew were trying to support Dave and me, but it was hard. I didn't know what to ask anyone to do to help; it was a helpless situation to be in. Once again I felt useless.

Life was hard. I was still trying to hold it all together; Dave was still doing exams and I felt that I had let him down too. All this stress at the worst time possible for any kid, although thinking about when would be a good time, never I suppose.

All I could do was wait for the next day and see what the Swan hospital was really like. I tried to put it all back in perspective; he was being looked after, but again it was a sleepless night as I had that same reoccurring nightmare -him screaming for help, just as he had the first time they had taken him away.

I tossed and turned all night knowing I couldn't rest till I saw him again.

Swan

I found Swan hospital easily enough; about a forty five minute drive, on the motorway mostly all the way, although it does take me through the junction of the M1 and M62; probably one of the busiest junctions on the whole motorway system. The hospital is made up of a large, old manor house with some modern wings attached, semi sort of purpose built; it looked ok and had nice gardens.

I walk into the old part of the building; the reception area was extremely spooky; a small room with large stained glass windows, very dark wood panelled walls and a green leather chesterfield sofa; having radio four piped out loudly through several speakers did nothing to lighten the atmosphere.
It was horrible, reminding me of a budget horror movie...especially after walking in from the brilliant sunshine of the second May bank holiday.

After booking in with the receptionist I waited over half an hour for a staff member to come and take me up to the ward. He reminded me of my sister's husband, Billy. He started chatting and I asked if it would still be a full hours visit; you had to book hour slots in advance and waiting for him and now getting up to the ward had taken 35 minutes of that hour, he said that they might let me stay a few minutes extra, I was starting to get a bad feeling about this place, it was world apart from the friendly reception I had got at Waterloo.

We went into the new building and up some stairs, arriving in a wide corridor with rooms going off either side. I could see Rex at the end of the corridor; they were making him wait there. Until they showed me into a little lounge; eventually letting him into the room. It had a small sofa and an armchair. I had a bag of goodies and as usual Rex wanted his daily Diet Coke fix. I gave him a small bottle and we shared it; sharing out various goodies too; Walker's cheese and onion crisps, again his favourite, with a mars bar to finish off. I know most of his favourite things after so many years together; I could take him a selection of his 'faves' every day without getting the same thing twice in one week.

This time he was different. When I had arrived at Waterloo although he had still been a bit confused and disorientated, he had responded to me very positively; this time he seemed quite distant I hate to say it but he looked a mess; he had really dark circles around his eyes, they were sunken into his head making my man look quite sinister; normally a sparkly bright blue they seemed dull and lifeless, they must have given him some heavy duty sleeping pills or medication last night.

Rex remembered being at home and straight away knew that he had scared me; that was why he was back in hospital. This time he remembered more of his stay in the police station, and he told me all about what had happened after I had left the house before the police turned up.

The same member of staff that had shown me up to the ward was now sat in the lounge with us; it wasn't very nice to be honest. I asked him why he needed to be in the room with us, after 20 years we don't need a chaperone. I can hardly get pregnant; he had the snip six years ago. The bloke said it was policy; I accepted it as in the past I had had to do this with volatile clients, but this was my husband and I was telling staff that I was safe, but they made the rules.

We would learn quickly that at this hospital they had rules, regulations and strict policies that would change with the staff on duty, and most of them were implemented dependant on whether the Ward Manager was on site; the staff seemed to be very wary of her.

The funny thing was that having seen Rex kick off hundreds of times in the last years, screaming and shouting had become a way of life; not scary at all most of the time. But I smiled as I knew he would have pooped his pants if Rex had started shouting, and probably ran from the room leaving me with Rex anyway.

The next thirty minutes ticked by quickly, many other patients wandered up and down the corridor. One particular guy came and peered through the window into the room several times; the staff member shouted quite loudly "Piss off you Dickhead"; I couldn't believe my ears. but he started laughing and said it again as the bloke outside the window stuck two fingers up at him.

If he spoke to one patient like that, I felt sure he could have spoken to them all like that.

My time was up and they made me leave, despite having nearly half of my hour wasted by waiting around for them to get me into the ward.

As I walked from the building I could hear someone banging gently on the window above my head. As I walked over to my car I could make out Rex's figure through the tinted windows; waving like mad. I hoped he was ok.

I was concerned about the leaving part, but this time he wasn't too far from home and I knew I would be coming everyday to see him; just to check he was being looked after properly.

It surely wouldn't take that long to sort out a little medication; then he would be home. He had been coping at home well enough and this place felt like a prison to me.

Rex had been asking for treatment, and section 3 was for use with people who would not comply with treatment.

As I walked in my phone was ringing; I picked it up to hear Rex on the other end, reminding me to book an appointment to visit the next day. You had to book early in a ward of about fifteen to twenty clients; they only had three one hour visiting slots in any one day so if you didn't book quickly you couldn't get in for a visit.

Realistically this meant that people got a maximum of one to two visits a week; that wasn't enough for us. I know the statistics for people with love and support getting better quicker than those without, and he was ill. I immediately rang and booked for the next day.

Whilst on the phone I also asked about booking in advance for the week but they insisted I had to ring everyday, it was like visit your sick husband lottery…

One of the nurses said that they understood how upsetting this was, but I still can't believe that it is a hospital stance on visiting; research really does show that supported people get better faster, so having such strict rules around visiting surely must have a serious affect on the wellbeing of patients. The saddest thing is, most people that end up on sections have little in the way of family support; living with someone with mental health issues isn't easy, as many people reading this will know, I think that's how they get away with it. Over the coming weeks it became apparent that these slots were taken by solicitors working to get people off their sections; even prisons put in extra visiting time for solicitors. Patients should be entitled to some level of respect and dignity; human rights should have allowed separate time slots for that to happen, but not here, they just took priority over family visits.

Over the coming weeks it became apparent that letting patients leave whether they were ill enough to be sectioned or not was not high on the agenda. One member of staff described the ward downstairs as a dumping ground for patients with nowhere to go, nobody to want them.

Why it would be, for a private hospital making so much money from local health authorities; with weekly charges in excess of a grand for a bed on a ward such as this, in a rush to discharge patients?

I work not twenty miles from this hospital, and spend a minimum of 40 hours a week evidencing how I spend the government funding provided to the charity for which I work. Health authorities getting away with spending money on shit like that makes my blood boil.

By my visit on Monday Rex was becoming very withdrawn, and started to take the pallor of a drug addict.

I know that look; as I have worked with many over the last years as well as having dealt with issues with drug abuse amongst family and friends; the grey, transparent skin and sunken eyes, slow movements and spaced-out perception of the world; all indicated that he was being over medicated.

That could quickly make him a 'Substance Addict' of the worst kind; a prescription junkie. No offence meant to anyone with the description I have used; it's just the best way to describe people kept on medication by doctors who should be giving psychological treatments instead.

I took my friend Sharon on Monday; she wanted to make sure he was ok. After all she had talked him through a manic period for about forty five minutes on Friday, and had been friends with him for the last 14 years. She wanted to check he was ok; she had been alarmed when I told her about the visit the night before.

During the visit Sharon questioned the nurses about Rex's care and their intentions for looking after him; she was extremely worried about the state he was in, the medication had quickly turned him into a Zombie and it worried her. I was glad it wasn't just me over-reacting. The nurse in charge that day told us that I would be able to come into ward round the next day if I wanted to; they would be discussing medication at that meeting. I was keen to attend; I was of course very interested in what they were going to be doing with Rex, to get him sorted out and back home to me and Dave as soon as possible.

If it was only going to be a couple of weeks I may get away with not bringing Dave here into this environment to visit his Dad; it was not going to be pleasant however both Dave and Rex were already asking to see each other.

I arrived at 10 am as they had told me to; here I had no right to book a visit to see Rex on ward round day. I could see him during his slot with the clinical team and that was that.

I waited and waited for someone to come down to reception to collect me; Rex knew I was coming and had tapped on the window to wave as I came in, but it was taking ages. This had sometimes happened at

Waterloo; obviously a group of doctors and therapists discussing patients well being could take some time, but in Waterloo this hadn't been an issue as I would wait with Rex and we could sit in the garden or have a cup of tea; talking about how he was doing whilst we were waiting. Here I was worried that Rex knew I was in the building, as he could see my car from his room window, but I wasn't allowed to wait with him; it is torture and I couldn't understand why he was being punished or "wound up" in this way..

Eventually, after almost two hours, a nurse came down to get me. I was taken into the room where yesterday's visit with Rex had been. I think it was the recreational room, as it contained a knackered, old table tennis table and a few chairs, and not much else, except a broken bed.

The people around the table introduced themselves Dr Alice was to be Rex's responsible medical officer. The one with the power to keep him detained, a forensic psychiatrist, a nurse, a ward doctor and the final person was the family social worker who worked full time at the hospital.

I asked when Rex was coming in and they said they had already seen him; saying that this was normal for his first ward round. I asked why the nursing staff had invited me to come if that was the case, to which I got no response. I was aware that Rex had seen me come in and go into the room; I was keen to get out of there I had no interest in chatting to this team; I had come to support Rex and if that wasn't possible I just wanted to visit for an hour and go.

I did answer their questions, I am not rude and I wanted to ask the social worker about arranging a visit for Dave to see his dad. She responded by telling me that if it was appropriate at anytime in the future Rex would be allowed supervised access to his son. I asked her what she meant by supervised and she explained that she would only be able to arrange a meeting if she could be there to watch over the visit. At that I asked to leave and see Rex.

The nursing staff said that I couldn't see him; I began to get upset. I had been waiting for hours and knew that Rex would be waiting to see me.

I mentioned this to the staff on the ward.

I had battled through rush hour traffic and for what? To be excluded from my husband's meeting with his doctors and denied a visit with him? I reminded them my husband was in hospital because he was sick; no one was able to explain why they were treating him like a forensic patient who had committed a crime.

Eventually they let me see him for a few minutes, I had to stand and argue to get to see him; the whole situation had affected Rex. He was very upset, and I wasn't leaving without a few minutes to hug him.

As we went into the room that they had cleared out for us I took a bottle of diet coke from my bag and passed it to Rex, he was obviously very thirsty as his mouth was going white around the edges. He looked dehydrated. A member of staff grabbed it from me and said that I was breaking the rules; no drinks could be brought into the unit as they may contain banned substances.

I started to laugh as I honestly thought they were winding us up. But no, it was in the rules today; no drinks, the last two days it had been ok but today… I tried explaining it was a sealed bottle of coke I had just bought; they still took it off me though.

They said Rex could buy them from the vending machine if he wanted a drink, I asked how much they were so I could make sure he had enough money, and started to laugh again as they explained a small bottle of diet coke came out of the vending machine for the princely sum of one pound twenty; two for a quid at our local co-op, but they were charging that. The robbing swines! This was a hospital robbing from the poor, Rex had no income and most patients survived on benefits in the system.

At least I understood why they didn't want me bringing it into the hospital; they were clearly making a lot of profit from selling people this stuff.

Anyway, a few minutes later, they came and told me I had to go. Rex was very confused about what the doctors had told him in Ward round, and I was unable to explain things as I had done during his previous stay at Waterloo, as the team here hadn't told me anything.

I left in tears, worried about how upset Rex had been by the whole situation. I booked a visit for the next day as I left the ward, and went home determined to find out when they would be sorting out his treatment closer to home, as they should have done the previous Tuesday when he had come home from Waterloo.

As soon as I got home I rang the local Matron again; she informed me that she would be dealing with it when she had time. I did get angry as it seemed once again that they were happy to pay for him to be detained in hospital rather than treat his illness. Surely just one week in a place like that would cost more than a month's treatment in the community?

She promised to sort out an assessment as soon as possible; I had to explain to this woman that as well as trying to deal with having a husband who has had some sort of breakdown; visiting him was crippling me financially. I didn't want to discuss my private business with her but in practical terms it had cost me over a grand to keep visiting him up to now, and I couldn't carry on forever.

I rang that night to chat to him; again a phone on the ward was useful for keeping in touch, although you had to be put through the office phone so that they could keep a record of who patients were talking to. It also restricted how much contact you could have with your loved one; a lot of the time they wouldn't answer the ward phone to put you through. I could hear the anxiety and upset in his voice, I don't think he could cope with this place as well as Waterloo; it was in a different league altogether. At Waterloo all effort had been concentrated on the patients need.

Today's fiasco with visiting and going into ward round together; it was clear this place obviously had a different outlook on treating people with mental health issues altogether.

I visited him the next day to find that they had restrained and medicated him. He had become upset the previous evening and started shouting, and they had told him to go to his room like a naughty boy. When he'd got into his room they slammed the door after themselves and held the handle so he couldn't leave, keeping him detained in his room for being anxious and upset about the day's events.

At that point he started jumping on his bed, he told me it was like being back in a police cell. When his bed had snapped they came in and removed it leaving him to sleep on the floor, I was outraged. I asked a member of staff about the incident and she confirmed his bed had been taken out of his room. Then I asked what they had done to support him after his traumatic day, to which the staff member said he was still being levelled and this was an important part of being looked after at this hospital. I asked what he meant by being levelled; I have never come across this before and I have worked in a lot of places; he went on to explain that all patients must learn how to behave so sometimes they were asked to go to their rooms or had things removed until they could behave properly. It was bloody barbaric.

I was astounded he was being treated this way; self discipline was always a strong point for Rex, obviously he had been upset but they wouldn't listen. Ninety nine percent of the time he did as he was told; easy to manage they said in Waterloo… His good self control had been used to help him get better at Waterloo according to the staff there; that was one of the things that they had welcomed.

I had worked in a unit that used behavioural therapy to modify behaviour, but we never made people sleep on the floor like animals, that wasn't caring for someone, it was an outrageous punishment for being anxious.

It had all started over him hitting the vending machine as it failed to give him his 30p change; so his small bottle of warm coke had cost him £1.50. I would probably have kicked it, and so would you…

As I looked around the recreation room I saw his bed was being stored in there; it was starting to look like a bed grave yard…As it joined the one already being stored there.

I asked if they were going to give it back; they said no. He could sleep on the floor until they thought he could behave properly. I was finding it hard to keep myself together whilst I was with Rex as I didn't want him to see how upset I was, but it was devastating seeing this happen to him; a war veteran and decent human being, in my mind he was being treated like a dog.

I spent the rest of the visit trying to be positive but Rex was drooling and hardly able to speak; they had given him even more medication.

I spoke to Rex that night and he was still upset about his bed. I tried to be as positive as possible but it was quite hard and Rex was flat; he had been bubbly and funny since he had come back from Greece, but within a few days of being admitted to the Swan he was as down and as depressed as I had ever seen him.

I checked my answer phone as I had been out for most of the day; to my surprise there was a message from our local hospital saying that they were going to assess him the next day. I hoped they would move him for many reasons, but most of all because he was clearly being abused there.

I rang Swan and asked if they knew Miss Red, a social worker from our local community mental health team, was coming down the next day. They said they did and I wondered why they hadn't mentioned it, but I was just thankful it was happening so I left it at that. They advised I rang back in the morning to speak to the ward manager if I wanted to come in for the assessment.

My visit was booked for two in the afternoon, and she was coming in the morning.

At least we were moving forward at long last; he had only been here for five days but it felt like a lifetime.

I rang the next day and was told by the ward manager, Tina, that I wasn't allowed down for the assessment and that I should grow up and stop being so silly; it was only an assessment. I couldn't think why she felt the need to be so rude to me.

I arrived after lunch for my visit and asked staff what had happened at the assessment. They said they didn't really know, I asked Rex and he told me that Miss Red had told him he would be back in his own local hospital as soon as possible. Hospital staff couldn't confirm or deny this as no one from Swan had sat in on the assessment. Rex had seen Miss Red and Tina eating lunch together in the staff area, but Tina said that she hadn't had chance to talk to her…
I still don't know what was really said, but I know that Rex had told her he was sleeping on the floor; this obviously didn't concern her or upset her enough for her to raise concerns to the ward staff as he still didn't have his bed back. I was fuming.
A Social worker looking after my husband's well being that wasn't concerned about Rex having his bed removed as a punishment wasn't really that shocking at that time; it just seemed that this was the level of care that they accepted, but it still seems wrong to me.

It was probably costing our local health authority a couple of hundred quid a night to keep him sleeping on the floor; if I had been that social worker I would have been disgusted and let them know.

By this time Rex was talking about being levelled and medication; I think the staff were talking to him about being good to get his bed back… again a very different approach from Waterloo, where they concentrated on his illness and getting him well. Here they just wanted him to conform to what they thought a quiet mad patient should be; no interest in him as a person.
He couldn't even butter his own toast as they wouldn't let them use a butter knife; he ate with plastic cutlery. It was a degrading and very strict regime within the ward.
Rex told me about several things that had upset him; such as an old guy who was on the ward. Since they weren't allowed belts, scarves,

dressing gown ties or anything such as that; this one guy's trousers would fall down every time he stood up. Rex was upset that the staff and other patients would find this very funny as the old guy stood there exposed; they would just laugh at him.

He had also witnessed several restraints but always on the smaller patients; not very often on the bigger, louder ones. Visiting time was over for the day and Rex made me promise to chase up what Miss Red had said and let him know the next day.

I reminded Rex that Fred would be coming to see him the next day so I wouldn't be able to come as well. He was happy enough, like I said he is close to my brother, so he would be pleased to have someone different to look at and talk to.

I booked the visit for Fred and Lisa once I got home; I prayed all the way that I could get a slot now he knew they were coming.

I rang Lisa and told her about the bed; she was very angry and said she would talk to them about it the next day. I said that he would probably have it back by then so she would need to check with Rex first.

Fred rang a short while later after talking to Lisa; he needed to check with me that what she had said was true. I told him about the bed and the assessment; I also reminded him he wasn't allowed to take any drinks in and he started laughing, asking who was going to stop him. I suppose being over 6ft and twenty stone did have advantages, but I did warn him knowing that he would take what he wanted into the hospital and woe betide anyone that tried to stop him; I didn't want Rex upsetting or kicking off.

I also warned him what to expect from Rex; he was seriously over-medicated.

If his little brother wanted diet coke he would get it. Now I was worried they would make a scene; but they just wanted what was best for Rex too. It didn't appear to us that what was on offer at this place was not good, let alone the best.

I got up the next day wondering if it was really a week since I had rang 999; in some ways it felt like a lifetime ago. The neighbour's curtains were still twitching - only Jim and Janet next door spoke to me.

Dave was coming to the end of his exams and was asking to see his dad; understandably he was upset. He had gone out to a party, come home to an armed raid that had ended with his dad being taken back to a police cell, and he missed him terribly even under normal circumstances let alone with such trauma attached to the last time he saw him. Whilst he had exams on I used that as an excuse not to go to the hospital, but he hadn't stopped nagging all week, and next week was his last exams; I would need to sort it out before then.

I didn't have to rush around to fit in a visit, so I was able to catch up with other things. I spoke to the hospital and they told me it would take a week or more for Miss Red's report to get to them, I guessed this would mean he was staying put for sometime yet.
I was glad I wasn't going to see him today, he was extremely keen to get out of that place and it was hard work going, but even harder having to leave him there. Knowing I had to tell him it was probably going to be at least another week that he would have to stay in that place was not news I wanted to deliver.

I rang my friend Daisy; she is a cook in a small school. I knew she would be starting work; it was about 10.30 and I thought she started soon but I hadn't spoken to her for ages; and she has a knack of putting things back in perspective, I was struggling to cope with everything; this week had been the hardest so far by a long way; the hospital was crap and seeing him detained and medicated like that was causing me to get depressed and stressed; keeping my chin up was getting harder. She was the person to cheer me up and chill me out.

As she answered her phone I could hear pots and pans clattering in the background, she was already at work. I told her what was happening and promptly burst into tears. I hadn't meant to, but it was one of

175

those things. I apologised for disturbing her at work and she told me to put the phone down and she'd be in touch soon.

All I could do was lie on my sofa and sob; I cried and cried. I thought my heart would break, why had I rang the police, I blamed myself over and over but I knew in my heart it wasn't me that had failed him; I had looked after him as well as I could for seven years, I wanted him looking after properly but it felt like that was never going to happen.

I lay there for sometime, it was the first day I had really started to feel sorry for myself, and for my husband and son. I don't like feeling sorry for us, it isn't a productive feeling, but I was finding it hard to stop crying.

Just as I started to calm myself down my back door opened, and in flew Daisy. She had food, drink and a massive hug for me. I don't think I have ever been so pleased to see someone so much in my life; she talked me through stuff and we must have drank about 100 cups of tea, but it really was just what I needed. She had walked out of work and travelled an hour and half to get to me; I was thankful once again to have such good friends.

I don't have hundreds, but the ones I do have are the best. She stayed all day and sorted me out. I love her so much even though we are an odd couple; her a tree-hugging, green hippy and me a respectable manager and housewife. I would, or could, have done something silly that day; back to the urge to go and kill someone at the local hospital.

When Rex rang later on, after Fred's visit, he was a bit brighter; I told him I would call him back at tea time.

Daisy was cooking as I sat down to make the call, and I could tell from Rex's voice as he answered the ward phone that he was upset. I asked what had happened and he said he had shouted at Tina, the 'Ward Witch' as we had called her, all because she had been rude to him; she had been aggressive and started pointing her finger in his face, shouting at him loudly in front of all the other patients and staff; it had upset him a lot. I wondered if my brother had upset her, but

176

apparently not, it was over something and nothing; she had made snide comments about him "needing" visitors' everyday. Why shouldn't he get visitors? We loved him and wanted to make sure he was ok. I couldn't understand why they would have a problem with visitors if they were looking after people the way they should be, but she appeared to be unnerved by a family that cares.

It was clear she would shout at anyone, patient, relative or staff. Half the staff on the ward would defend her, the other half condemned her; but she was in charge and boy did everyone have to bow down to her. Once more I was worried that this stay in hospital was doing more harm than good.

I came off the phone and Daisy suggested getting onto the Mental Health Commission website to have a look at what standards they had in place to protect people like Rex, who were being detained in this way, it didn't help a lot, but it did give me a number to ring; it was too late today but I would be in touch first thing on Monday.

As we ate tea we all sat and chatted. Dave loves Daisy too, and was enjoying off loading to someone else I think.
Despite being very upset I was feeling more optimistic; Daisy had given me the boost I needed. I hugged her as she left and again thanked god for good friends.

Fred rang and I knew he was angry, the place was a hole and Rex wasn't settled there like he had been in Waterloo; both registered as Hospitals in the same way, having the Authority to detain patients held under section, but this was like a prison.
They seemed to want to make life hard; no kind words for families trying to cope at a very difficult time, and no treatment for patients being detained to receive it.
I decided that I would take other people to see him just so that I would have witnesses to the appalling treatment he was receiving.

Dave and I sat talking late into the night; we are so lucky having such a fantastic child, we laughed and joked and I tried hard to lighten the mood. This time last week I had been sat in a police car for three hours with an armed raid going on around my house, things could never get to that point again. We joked about getting a straight jacket and chains to secure him to the breakfast bar if another situation occurred.

The day ended well, except for the dark thoughts that kept creeping in to my head about my poor man being treated in this way, he is a war veteran after all, fighting the governments, wars, gets you no preferential treatment in this country.

The next day dawned and another visit to organise; my sister was coming with me today. Dave was quite annoyed, he wanted to see his dad, but they were both adamant that they did not want a supervised visit. A game of football, a picnic lunch, a nice few hours together like they had had in Waterloo, but it wasn't going to happen in this place. Dave had loved watching his Dad doing cartwheels in the garden at Waterloo.

Mandy and I arrived at the hospital, and once again, we were made to wait for nearly 30 minutes before being let onto the ward. My sister was losing patience as the nurse came down to take us to the ward; this time she asked if the visit would be lengthened accordingly, but the same response as last time was that it wasn't up to them; the Ward Manager had given instruction that our visits had to be just that hour; what hour?

Having not seen Rex for two days I was shocked by how rough he looked; he was drooling and slurring his words. He had been given heavy duty medication again and began telling us how it had knocked him out; he felt crap and wasn't making much sense. I was surprised; when Mandy demanded a nurse came in to answer some questions, before I could get a word in she was asking a lot of questions, and suggesting Rex wasn't medicated in this way again.

At last I was sure it wasn't just me over reacting; she has known Rex for the last 20 years and she was very upset by the conditions he was in.

The nurse on duty that day, George, actually agreed and said he would make a note on Rex's file for this not to be given again.

The visit did run over the hour, but at last there was a chink of light at the end of the tunnel; this nurse seemed to care, he was the first one in there that I had met.

The next day it was me and Jamie that went to visit, and he was a bit brighter, at least more with it and they had let him have a walk in the grounds for 15 minutes so he was feeling a little better.

Those two spent the hour eating sweets, and drinking smuggled in coke whilst playing table tennis; they have always been close and I think Jam was trying to distract him and keep him busy so she wouldn't worry about how ill he looked, it was a pity the bats were broken and the ball well dented, but they struggled through.

Rex was still confused about why he had to be locked up to be looked after; he was accepting treatment, had been asking for treatment and just wanted to get home. Five weeks in hospital is a long time for anyone. We discussed me coming in for his ward round this week; last week they had fobbed me off saying that they needed to meet him by himself, but I wouldn't let that happen this week. Again I was told that it started about 10.30 and this week we would be asking all the right questions, I didn't think he should be sectioned in my heart; we had lived with this illness for long enough and with the right treatment and support we could easily cope at home.

The visit was good but again I was sad to have to leave him there, knowing he was being driven mad by being cooped up and to be fair some of the patients did seem quite demanding and full on; extremely ill people. That's obviously why they were so strict, but Rex didn't need to be there.

Monday arrived, he had been detained for nine days and other than over medicating him they had still not started any proper treatment.

I contacted the mental health act commission, thinking that they would be interested in people being detained just for needing treatment.

I spoke to them at length and they agreed that if it was true that Rex had been asking for treatment, and would be willing to stay in a local hospital for treatment if necessary, then there certainly was no need to keep him locked up.

They suggested I apply to have Rex discharged. I had to write a letter to Dr Alice, as she was the one who was authorising his detention. They also advised me to get a solicitor. I was amazed; he had committed no crime, he hadn't hurt anyone, but they could keep him locked up for as long as they liked. I spoke to a specialist mental health solicitor and they told me what to put in the letter requesting his discharge.

I went off for a visit at the hospital and still he was being medicated heavily by the staff, one nurse in particular had been dealing with Rex, his named nurse, Melonhead or something, she was called. Unlike Dexter at Waterloo she hadn't bothered asking questions about Rex and the family, and his illness, she had introduced herself and then only turned up to give him medication; no talking therapies such as he had got used to, no interest in what his problems were, he was becoming flatter every day. He has had serious bouts of depression in the past and it continued to worry me.

I told him what the solicitor had said and, as I left, promised him I would bring the letter in that was needed to start the ball rolling to get his section lifted. It was ward round tomorrow and I was determined to get some answers. I could give the letter directly to Dr Alice.

As I pulled into the car park the next day at 10.30am Dr Alice pulled in beside me in her brand new Jag; they must pay well here as I had seen her in a sports car last week.

She didn't look at me or smile, she just walked past. I knew they would be waiting for her to start ward round so I took a seat and made myself ready for a long wait. I knew she had seen me so I hoped they would put Rex near the start of the round and not keep me waiting like they had last week. Little did I realise that this day I was to wait over three hours until they came down to get me; Rex was extremely angry when I was shown into the ward; he knew how long I had been made to wait. Yet he was in control of his emotions; I would have expected him to start ranting about it but he was so well medicated he just apologised on the hospitals behalf!

I thought he was supposed to be the patient... It should have been the staff saying sorry not my poor man; I was pretty sure Dr Alice had made me wait on purpose, but I'd never be able to prove it so…

I had handed my request to have Rex discharged to the doctor at the reception area on my way into the hospital.

Dr Alice had it in front of her. George, the nice nurse was there, as well as other therapists and doctors, and Tina the evil ward manager. The letter was full of Rex's history, how long he had been ill, how many times he had tried to get treatment, and how much we both understood and wanted the right treatment for him, but it also stated quite clearly that this hospital didn't seem to be what he needed. Over the years Rex had been institutionalised by the Army environment; the last thing he needed was to go through this hospital's strict regime for any longer than necessary. I knew that they would need to give him medication to stabilise his mind but this was nearly two weeks of drug therapy and nothing else, he needed more than drugs.

Dr Alice started to speak before we even got sat down; saying straight away that Rex would not be discharged from his section, and that she felt it was inappropriate that I asked for it. I was gob smacked; she went through the conversation I had had with the commission yesterday, the advice from the solicitor, my reasons for requesting his release and she looked me in the eye and said no.

I knew what I had been told about my responsibility as his next of kin, and his rights as a patient, but she was not prepared to discuss them. She quickly moved the subject on to another issue which was the medication. Rex started to talk and put his points forward, mentioning the over medication on several occasions, not least at the weekend when it had wiped him off his feet, George backed up what he was saying and Melonhead wrote down the information in what I assumed was his support plan or nursing notes. Dr Alice stated the medication in question must not be given again.

Once Rex had finished talking to them about his medication, we moved on to asking for a visit for Dave, again they insisted that it would need to be supervised by the Social Worker even though they agreed that they would now allow Rex to leave the hospital grounds with a staff member to go to the shop or out for breakfast at the local café. I hoped this meant that he would be able to see Dave without the need for a social worker to be there but they wouldn't agree.

The next thing we asked was when they were going to start his proper treatment, you know, counselling, and therapy stuff like that. Dr Alice turned to us and informed us that she didn't feel this was the right place for him to start treatment as this ward is not a therapeutic ward.

I asked if there was another ward he could be moved on to and she said no, I was getting confused; I know that using a Section 3 is about admitting someone to hospital because they need treatment but here she was saying they don't provide it on this ward, that must be illegal…or immoral probably both actually.

Dr Alice went on to say that she felt Rex would be better closer to home, in a less secure environment, but that we would need to wait for our local hospital to sort this out. This ward definitely wasn't the right place for him to start receiving treatment she made that very clear.

By the end of the ward round I was very angry but tried to keep a lid on it; they were letting us out together for a walk, with a member of staff within touching distance of Rex!!! Lovely, the first time we had been allowed out together for ten days.

It did cross my mind to just put him in the car and go, but my little old Suzuki only does 80 down hill with the wind behind him; I didn't think we'd get that far. The hospital was halfway down a steep hill and I knew they would catch us on foot before we got to the traffic lights; I knew that this place was just looking for an excuse to stop me from visiting

I left Rex feeling a bit better, and with some money to get a newspaper and stuff from the shop the next morning when he was to be allowed. His daily half hour walk to the shop should give him something to distract himself, he was dying to get his hands on a newspaper but it would only happen if they had enough staff to do it, and there was never that many staff on duty…

Again I contacted our local health service when I got home to let them know what had been said. I asked the Matron to get him in to a more suitable place, preferably closer to home somewhere they could start treating him. The nice lady that dealt with my earlier complaint was on holiday, so it was back to the matron and she was a nasty bit of work. Many friends who had worked at the local hospital had all been telling me stories about her and how disliked she was; I realised I had started to beg and was being extremely nice to this woman, playing a game to try and get the issues resolved and she was just dismissing me like I was complaining about not having a dentist, or maybe getting the wrong colour plaster on a cut finger. But the care package they had him on was not right for him; she didn't care and she refused to listen. I felt very let down; our hospital was refusing to care for him.

Wednesday morning, I am feeling brighter. He rang to say he was going to the local shop and he would see me later that afternoon; I couldn't wait. He had been locked in that ward for days and now he would be at least seeing more people; that should cheer him up a bit.

Before I had chance to get on the road for my daily trek to the hospital he had rang fuming; he had bought a Sun newspaper, a bottle of coke and a cigar at the shop under the watchful eye of a staff member, only to have them confiscated on his return to the ward. The explanation given to him was that the Sun wasn't allowed on the ward because of page 3… Grown men not allowed to look at page 3 boobs !!!

The cigar could have something in it!!!

And coke has to come from the machine for £1.20…
Why on earth the member of staff that had gone with him had allowed him to buy stuff that was classed as contraband is beyond me; I could have understood if he had gone by himself but this was a joke. Either that or they were trying to wind him up so he would kick off, that way they could have justified keeping him locked up.
As it stood there had been a couple of small incidents in his first days; when he had punched the vending machine because it was a rip off, then he'd broken his bed, which I know was caused by them keeping me waiting for hours to visit that day and then refusing to let me see him. Attempting to lock him in his room for his "behaviour" the same day had wound him up.
The argument when Tina had pointed in his face and shouted at him, I think he was doing too well, but they knew they needed to justify having him locked up in their care. They seemed to want to wind him up.

By the time I got there my husband had watched all the staff read his paper in the staff office; but he wasn't allowed to catch up on the world cup, gossip…Or do the crossword, he has been reading that paper for 20 years and now he wasn't allowed. Looking at page 3 had always been described as stress relief whilst he'd been away on his tours; the Sun had always gone with the troops; like a bible. Now he wasn't allowed to read it.

The Great Escape

Over the next days I contacted everyone I could think of to try and get him moved; I even looked into paying for him to go to a private hospital, but in reality I didn't have the money to pay for that. I was struggling to keep up with 20 quid a day for petrol to get to see him, let alone the amount of money needed to keep him in coke and fags, but that was still a lot less than £200 a night to have him moved to better hospital. I was still off work, and money was tight. In our household we'd lost 25k a year when he'd left work, I'd never catch up on one wage...

I got in touch with our local MP, his assistant passed on a message to me that I could contact Combat Stress, a charity running as a voluntary Organisation; giving support to veterans. I rang to ask them to look at the poor practice by the NHS that was happening in his constituency, to Soldiers that have fought his government's wars...
It's a joke, an MP suggesting charity rather than expect care from your local hospital; what a prat.

It was on my visit to the doctors this week that saw my diagnosis turn from stress and exhaustion to reactive depression; the first time in my life that this has ever been diagnosed, or a major problem. Like I have said previously I'm no different to anyone, we all have bad days, sometimes weeks, that's just life. But this was different; I could feel the dark cloud over my head and it felt like a ton weight. Crying was becoming an hourly occurrence, my doctor wanted to give me some anti-depressants but I turned down her kind offer; hoping instead to either control it myself, or maybe try a herbal remedy. I was seeing her weekly and I was also desperate to get back to work. I knew that having nothing but my own problems to think about was doing me no good, but after 6 weeks off work I was feeling crap; having a job that provides support for vulnerable people has always kept things real for me, some people have real problems.
My doctor agreed to let me try to sort it out myself, but not to go back to work. She asked if I would come back the next week just so she

could keep an eye on me. She had done a small test and I think my depression was severe, but I was extremely frustrated at having to witness this situation; with my husband getting worse, not better. But I knew, eventually, it would get resolved. Things always get better eventually; I certainly didn't want to start taking tablets that took weeks to start working as I truly hoped and believed that his situation would start to get better in the coming weeks.

I had received a letter from Swan stating that an independent Mental Health tribunal would be held at the hospital at the end of June; that was only a couple of weeks away. I could cope until then if it wasn't sorted out; then I would need something from my doctor; I accepted that. Still in my heart I knew he wasn't mad enough to section, I trusted the judgement of the team at Waterloo and they had assessed him for 22 days, he had a small wobble with his mental health lasting for about 30 minutes, two weeks ago and now they had him on so much mood stabilising medication that I could have probably stood, beating him to death with a salmon and he wouldn't have raised an eyelid. We would get him home at the tribunal if Dr Alice, or our local hospital, hadn't sorted something out before then.

I left the doctors and went to buy some St Johns Wort. I have heard many good things about this herbal remedy over the years, so I started taking it just to help me out. They looked like giant rabbit droppings and took some swallowing, but anything had to be better than becoming a prescription junkie. Too many people are sat at home on medication for poor mental health and I couldn't afford to become one of them. Still no disrespect to anyone in that situation, trust me I know how hard it is to cope, but many of the drugs they hand out are as addictive as heroin or cocaine... I had a mortgage to pay, and a kid to support, Rex had no income for the last 18 months either; I couldn't leave him with nothing.
I had to keep going for all of our sakes, so a giant rabbit dropping every morning it was.

It was Friday and two weeks since the police incident; and still no local treatment. But I wasn't going to be beaten; me and Dave had some tea together and sat chatting about stuff. Dave spoke about visiting his dad at the weekend, and we came up with the idea of booking him into visit as my nephew; he was just 18 and we were going to use his identification to get Dave in. That way, the visit wouldn't have to be supervised by the social worker and it would be a more relaxed visit; but Dave bottled out at the last minute.

He just wanted his dad to hug, not all this deception and heartache, just a massive cuddle from his dad. At 16 and 10 stone he still sits on his dad's knee for a cuddle, or I might find them curled up together on the sofa watching a film, he didn't need to be upset by the environment, and I let him make his own decision.

He decided to stay away from the hospital for the time being; they were talking on the phone most days; it wasn't the same. I think Dave had got used to living with his mad dad and even though it had sometimes been hard work living with Rex's illness, he missed him like mad, wanting him home was all he wanted, the same as me.

I think that going to the hospital had been part of the problems causing my depression, and I didn't want him subjected to that. It really was a grim place to go, it got me down and I was only allowed in for an hour a day.

This weekend my sister was coming to visit again. As we drove over she had me stopping at every shop; Mandy adores Rex, as all of my family do but she had spent about 20 quid on goodies for him and was still buying more...

He was keeping some of the guys without families and visitors, or money, in goodies, that is just the way he is and she didn't care as long as he had everything she could lay her hands on. It was a boiling hot day and she got herself a chocolate bar to keep her going, as we drove down the motorway a big blob of chocolate fell out of the packet straight down her leg, I couldn't stop laughing as she looked like she had pooped herself, I only stopped laughing as I noticed it all over my car seat. It was the first time I had laughed in weeks.

She is one of the loves of my life, but dizzy doesn't come near it; we laughed and laughed through the visit as she went mad about the state of the hospital; she is a clean freak and the hospital wasn't the cleanest place I have ever been in.

Rex told me to have a day off the next day; I think he could see how stressed I was getting, I didn't arrange an appointment and the next day as I woke feeling guilty, I rang for a slot to be told there weren't any left.

I spoke to Rex, He asked why I hadn't been able to book an appointment to visit, I explained that because I had left it too late there weren't any spaces left. Rex said he felt sure that only one person had a visitor that day and there were supposed to be three slots, again I wasn't sure if this was done to wind us up.

Now we were at the start of week three.

The weeks passed by slowly, the next couple of weeks were a round of visiting and getting organised. I needed to get him some money coming in and I rang the benefit helpline. They said he would be entitled to incapacity benefit and maybe Disability Living Allowance, they sent out the packs. It helped to be doing practical stuff, it saved sitting around feeling depressed and anxious about stuff like I had been in those first two weeks he was in that place, or rather the over use of drugs to control him in those weeks that had made me loose the plot. Watching that happen to someone you love is devastating, but it was starting to pass as I gathered my strength to get our lives sorted out again…

I contacted various charities and also the Veterans Agency to claim his pension; I had found out through the website, the internet makes life much easier doesn't it? He should be entitled to some extra money from his pension fund through the Army.

That's when I met Helen, the welfare officer… she listened to our story and I saw the look of horror in her face; what our family had been through. Trying to live with this illness was wrong; we had tried to get help for Rex in the past four years, and if the government cared more he could have been getting the right help four years ago, when his PTSD had first been suggested as a possible diagnosis by our psychology department. Being in an extremely high risk group should have triggered the right treatment, but it hadn't and our lives had been affected dreadfully...

My husband is a good man who has kept his vows to me as well as being a good dad, and member of our extended family for many years before he developed this illness; it breaks my heart to remember how it used to be.

I could never have left him alone; he has needed looking after part time for four years and fulltime for the last two since leaving work, but remember we had been together 20 years by this stage.

When he had to leave work he was unable to cope, he had felt he'd been abandoned by everyone, he had become so ill he hid from the world, unable to cope and after all our years together, now was not the time to walk out on him, but I did consider it, I am not a saint.

It took hours of filling in forms and phone calls to various people to get the forms completed, but eventually they were all sent off and I hoped he would get some money in, mine was running out fast. I did wonder though how many "patients" would be able to fill in that amount of paperwork if they didn't have someone to help fill them. It made me miss work, filling in forms and supporting people like Rex is what my staff do; it's a bloody worth while job.

I also continued to speak to our hospital; to try and get him a bed back in our local area, but it wasn't happening, they just weren't interested I stopped letting it stress me out.

I also spoke to the solicitor to prepare for the Independent Review Panel, he would have been in this place for just over 5 weeks by the time the date for that came round, but it was our only chance of getting him out and I couldn't mess it up, it still concerned me that he was willing to accept treatment and shouldn't be locked up in the first place.

I wrote down everything that had happened over the last years; all the evidence I needed to prove that we could live with and cope with Rex at home. This wasn't the right environment for him to get better, now they had settled down his drug therapy, using mood stabilising medication; they had him doing occupational therapy groups. He was mostly the only person on the ward that bothered going to the groups, he even went to the smoothie making group… He was bored stiff, and getting more depressed by the day about his current situation; he goes down hill fast when he's flat. Part of Rex's "problem" is that he can't deal with Trauma very well, and what had happened to him over the past weeks had been extremely traumatic for him. This wasn't helping.

We prepared the case and by week four they had agreed that he should come home for a visit to let him see Dave on his home ground… Sense at last, but they needed to get some staff to agree to work extra hours to do it on the Saturday morning. Rex rang to say that it was organised; two guys that worked on nights had agreed to do it. They had got to know him, they understood our situation and were desperate for him to get this home visit; our family was wobbly, it needed time together.
I am not going to name them but they will know who they are, and I will be ever thankful for how much they cheered us all up. I don't know if they still work there, or if they've moved on but if I was them I wouldn't want to be associated with that hole.

They laughed as they listened to Rex on the phone, ordering ingredients to make them both breakfast during their trip to our house. Most people who know us would confirm him as a good 'brekky' chef; we have breakfast parties like others have dinner parties. It's his thing! He had only been allowed to use a blender under strict supervision; he was dying to get his hands on the cooker.

The trip home passed without a hitch; the smile on my two men's faces were a picture, I thought they might squeeze each other to a pulp. We were all well fed and he went back to the hospital with all his trust and faith in me to sort out his tribunal the following week.
I spoke to the matron again and again, asking them to move him and look after him because of how unsuitable this place was, but they still

didn't offer any help, they said a guy called Andy would be coming to the tribunal hearing on Thursday; a social worker I think… I don't think she thought he'd get out. She'd convinced herself that I was as mad as him. What she should have been thinking was I was strong and knew what was happening, and he had a "controllable" illness; that they needed to look after him not lock him up. I felt like a scratched record repeating myself. I am sat here wondering if she had a hearing problem.

I arranged to meet Rex's solicitor before the hearing. Just so you know the reason they hold these hearings it is to try and stop patients being held under the Mental Health Act inappropriately, they are monitored by a commission so I suppose that means the government again!!!
We had only just got copies of the nursing reports and we needed to run through the risks they had highlighted; remember the criterion that needs to be met for this act to be used; to be a danger to self or others, and/or lack insight about your illness, refusing treatment could also cause enough concern to detain someone. So what did they have to say in his report?

I'll list them in order so they you can cast your mind back over the things I have told you about his stay.

1. Rex punched the vending machine

2. Verbal Aggression towards staff, one incident; namely the finger wagging bully of a ward manager, Tina…

3. Snapped a plastic knife, after being told by staff they are unbreakable… what a challenge to a bored man…

Throw away the key… Anyone who committed such acts should be detained forever…. Dr Alice stated clearly that she felt he should remain on a section based on those facts; like they were good enough reasons. She did however state she felt he would benefit from being closer to home in a more relaxed environment. It was clear that she would be happy to keep him locked up until that was offered by our local hospital. I wondered when that would be; they had had him locked up for nearly ten weeks in total surely they have had time to sort out something.

These incidents had all happened over four weeks ago in his first week. There was no mention of his recent successful home visit, no mention of his now unescorted trips to the shop and around the grounds... The solicitor reassured me that there would be no problem getting him out. George the nice nurse from the day shift told me not to get my hopes up because no one normally leaves through the tribunal system here.

Two of the panel members came out and introduced themselves; they were both retired officers from the Armed Forces, both asked if I had been in touch with all the forces charities for help.

Andy turned up from our local health authority and introduced himself, my palms sweated as the meeting started.

The three panel members asked both sides to put their cases forward and listen carefully to all the facts.

They asked lots of questions and then turned to Andy, they asked direct the questions I had been asking for weeks; when were our local authority going to provide some treatment for him, Andy could not answer the question.

They called a break and said they needed to discuss some things they had heard.

Thoughts ran through my head, I really wanted him to get the best treatment; I knew he needed a lot of help and I wasn't strong enough to look after him by myself, but I couldn't leave him locked up for just being bonkers.
Within ten minutes they called us back into the room, they had made a decision just as they were asking the last few things the meeting was

interrupted by the receptionist. I'd got to know them well over the last few weeks; she had a message from Ann, the matron at our local hospital, they had miraculously found a bed. Two minutes before they were going to deliver their "verdict" at the panel the local authority had offered him a bed.

The chairman told us the decision; he was free to leave the hospital and make his own decisions about his care and treatment in the future.

Dr Alice and Andy started putting pressure on Rex to agree to go to our local hospital as a voluntary patient; it was his choice, the panel had said so, but I had to stand by his decision to decline their offer due to the poor service he had so far. Neither of us trusted that they wouldn't lock him up again, they should be pleased; I would be taking the burden, they just needed to provide cheaper community support. What could I say he was coming home again.

He went back to the ward with George to pack up his stuff; the panel members came over to me as I sat on a bench waiting for the last time… They all made me cry as they started praising me for looking after him, and standing by him, they didn't mean to make me cry; I was just relieved that they independently, based on facts, agreed with me. He just needed help, and now it was back down to me to provide it, but that was going to be easier than what had been happening.

They walked away, more people listening to our story in disbelief… I tried to establish if they were tears of joy or relief but I managed to stop them and prepare myself for his big departure. I could see the difference in him already as we sat together waiting for his medication; they didn't think he'd be going so they hadn't sorted out a prescription for him.

I sat working out that I had probably spent 34 hours visiting Rex at this hospital, probably 60 hours travelling back and forth and over 40 waiting in these grounds… That works out to a part time job over the weeks that I had to do it.

We got in my little old jeep and once again set off for home.

He knew what he needed to do; we talked about the private treatment we had been sorting out. Our GP had written the letter, our local branch of SSAFA, the Soldiers Sailors Air Force Association another charity had promised to help us find the money to pay for it. We just needed to wait for an appointment. The NHS had a duty to look after him too since they had used the section; that's the law. So they might come up with some treatment too. I was tired out and stressed to the max, but it was helping keep the depression at bay.

Dave was waiting on the doorstep.

Treatment

World cup fever has left the country; poor Rex had spent the whole time locked up in that place. He has missed the lot; the only positive for me was I hadn't had to go through the pain of watching. June is coming to an end and the sun is shining; I get him busy in the garden the very next day mowing and weeding and trying to keep him busy.

Andy was going to ring to arrange an appointment for the next week; he had promised, he wasn't mad enough to lock up but they still had a duty to look after him under the Law they had used to lock him up. He needed treatment, therapy… It was late afternoon before he called to make an appointment, promising to come on Monday.

The weekend passed peacefully; I quickly realised how much he slept on his medication although he had to get up at seven thirty everyday in hospital, I left him in bed to recuperate after his strict regime… an earthquake couldn't wake him.

Monday came round and I woke him up "early" at noon in time for Andy's visit. We waited and waited, eventually he called to say he was running 45 minutes late.

A couple of hours later he rang to say he couldn't make it; he would come the next day at 11. I knew that he wouldn't turn up. I'd realised in the last weeks how bad our local services are.

Everything was ok; Rex was settled, Dave and I thought he seemed to be a bit over medicated. I hadn't noticed it so much whilst he was in hospital; it was a boring place, I put his lethargy down to his environment, it really was hard work getting him going, a walk to the shop was about as far as we had got. For the last six weeks he'd had to sit around a boiling hot ward for twenty three hours a day, he'd lost his confidence to go out by himself.

There was a lot of stuff to organise; I wanted him to see our GP. He is the only doctor I could trust in our city and Rex liked him... He was also supporting our attempt to get treatment privately; making a referral to the place I used to work, and we needed to chase that up. I knew the local health service couldn't provide the treatment he needed.

In the mean time and after a lot of arguments with the local hospital's matron, and conversations with the complaints officer at the PCT, a meeting had been set up for me to meet the senior managers' from the local Primary Care Trust, the people responsible for the provision of the service Rex had received in the last weeks. I had a lot of questions I wanted answers to. I was still having nightmares about the night he was carried out of their hospital after only two and a half hours "care". I knew how much we had been through to get him into their care, a week being looked after by Wayne, John and our other friends in Greece, thousands of miles across Europe, six hours care by Easy Jet staff and Fred, two days at home with a total of about eight hours spent in A&E... No problems and then I had to witness that. It was a disgrace, the meeting was happening this Friday and I couldn't wait.

Andy turned up the next day and said that an appointment with the Consultant Psychiatrist had been arranged for Friday; Rex's face fell as he realised he had heard the name before; Dr Nopal was to be in charge of his care again. The same man who'd suggested he'd be ok if he gave up weed years ago, he'd put Rex off asking for help in one little appointment. He'd told the truth about his whole illness and the stupid man told him he was a druggie. Let's get it straight at this stage in this book the god's honest truth is, he did have issues with drink, from 1999 through to about 2004, he'd only ever drink occasionally, but when he did he would be unable to control himself or the vast amounts he'd consume in a short space of time ...
He gave it up two years ago completely, maybe drinking two beers at barbies or parties, but he says he doesn't like the taste that much any more... And as for Drugs, occasional use of cannabis to chill out at stressful times had not caused this problem, it had just made him easier to live with for the last few years since he'd realised how much the

excessive drinking hurt everyone around him. He needed something else. To be honest, it is extremely hard to get from trusted sources and that has limited the use extremely. I don't think it would see him classified as a "habitual drug user", so I just hoped the doctor had learnt some new ways of treating people since there last encounter.

Andy said that he would make sure that the time didn't clash with my meeting. I wondered how he knew about my meeting as I hadn't told him; he must have been informed by the complaints people. He said he wanted me to come to the appointment with Rex on Friday; I couldn't wait to meet Dr Nopal.

The week passed; getting Rex out and about sorting him out, it was 'around the clock' work getting him going, he'd have slept around the clock if me and Dave hadn't been there to wake him up…

Friday morning, I am up and out early for my meeting; he was with the consultant at 11.30. As I walked into my appointment I was on the phone to Dave, making sure he had got his dad up to come down to the hospital.
It was like military precision between me and Dave to co-ordinate his care.

I wish I had never gone to that meeting, I am used to working with these " professionals", many of the services I have managed in the last few years have had a lot of interaction with PCT'S and Mental Health Services, so meeting with managers comes as second nature. The people in that room wound me up beyond belief. I asked questions about the service they had provided for Rex, to try and establish what had gone wrong in the two and a half hours in their care the first time. They answered me by talking about the standards they aimed to achieve, saying collectively how they were trying to improve things, not mentioning that in the last two years they had actually failed to meet the standards set for mental health services in our area. I'd read their last audit information before coming to the meeting and gathered evidence of other failings in Mental Health Services locally; they would not speak directly about what had happened to Rex, I don't think they even knew who he was.

I then asked further questions about why his records weren't checked the second time he needed to come into hospital, anyone looking at his most up to date history should surely have been able to suggest something better than a trip back into A&E, after the previous trip into our local hospital had caused him such distress. This triggered a long explanation about the fantastic new computer system they had installed across the county to track people to stop them from falling through the net and getting crap treatment; they even went as far as telling it had cost about thirty five grand if I remember rightly.
They didn't laugh or appreciate my sense of humour when I suggested that they should try switching it on occasionally, as that obviously hadn't worked in Rex's case either.

They were so woolly and unaware of the impact their hospital's incompetence was having on extremely ill patients and their families at their most vulnerable time; it made me sick.

I walked out thinking about talking to the Medical Negligence solicitor down in Manchester, whose name we had been given by the Mental Health Solicitor that helped get him out of Swan. I had only expected a small apology, maybe an offer to reimburse some of my out of pocket expenses, but all I got was spin and sales patter about what they wanted to do in the future.
I rushed over to the other side of the hospital to meet Dr Nopal, the day could only get better.

I saw Rex waiting outside the doctor's office; I sat next to him and he grabbed my hand looking worried, like he was going into a lions den.

Andy turned up and we went in; Dr Nopal was a small man, about 5ft tall. His accent was very strong, and it was extremely hard to understand what he was saying. I felt rude having to keep getting him to repeat himself, I imagined the frustrations people had trying to understand him, it's a good job I have been bought up to be polite.

He asked about what had happened in the last weeks for about 5 minutes; he had obviously flicked through some notes because straight away he referred to the slight trace of cannabis in Rex's urine on his return from Greece. Rex explained that he had smoked one spliff with a friend a few days before the attack in Greece. He also told Nopal it had never caused any psychological problems in the past when he'd smoked it.

Next he asked about drinking, Rex explained that he had drank and smoked, a little pot in the past, but felt his problems were caused by his illness, not his use of substances. His Cannabis and Alcohol use had lessened over the years as his illness got worse; we both know enough to know that no substance is good for you. Both addicted to nicotine for years but other than that no vices, well maybe Revels could count... As for the substances everyone needs a crutch sometimes; drink then cannabis had been his, there is no denying that, but not the cause of his problems.

The doctor moved on, not appearing to take much notice of what Rex had just been saying, he asked what was causing the stress now. Rex obviously mentioned money and our current situation, especially me being responsible for him full time with no regular support on offer; everyday life was hard work and he felt terrible as he had no money. Other than that he had no stress.

He made a note of what medication had been prescribed at Swan and said he would monitor how it was working over the coming months again, ignoring Rex as he explained he could hardly get out of bed whilst he was taking so much. That had been fine in hospital, sleeping helped combat the boredom, but now he needed to start living again not snoozing.

Life is too short to sleep it away and far too precious to miss; even bad days are good because they make you feel alive, on this amount of mood stabiliser he couldn't feel anything.

As we left, Dr Nopal offered no way forward, no treatment, no advice and no hope. He basically told me to take him home and sort him out especially his debts...

What he expected me to do was beyond me; he'd clearly not listened to the bit where I told them I had sorted out all of the debts, mortgage, bills; juggling money calling in debts to cover all the outgoings on one wage instead of two. I'd even got benefit claims in for Rex, it was not having money coming in that was a problem for him, not what was being paid out, we have always paid all of our own bills. I about had a bloody break down trying to keep up with everything and he had no idea.

That didn't stop him from giving me advice about it rather than looking at what he could do for my husband as his doctor. I wonder if a doctor treating a heart attack would get away with telling his partner to go home and pay the bills instead of treating the broken heart... I hope not, you'd die waiting for your visa to be paid off...

Over the coming weeks his incapacity benefit started coming through, wealth beyond his wildest dreams...a whole fifty four quid a week... He was just about keeping his head above water but not contributing anything financially to our home. I was still standing all the bills and the mortgage by myself, but he was doing ok. I was taking all the pressure off him, desperately trying to stay positive. Dave had his application in for college; everything had started to calm down. Once again I started to think about going back to work; I needed to get back into the real world. I wasn't looking forward to going back; I hadn't forgotten the stuff that had been happening there just before all this had happened. Like being made redundant "by mistake", and being bullied by senior managers had also taken its toll on me; I figured it was better to go back there. The other option was losing my house due to being unable to pay my mortgage.

I felt quite trapped; my choices limited by the fact that I had no energy to find another job, the money was quite good with my place and the work, very rewarding, it's a pity the management structure is pants.

By the start of August I am planning to return to work and Rex has his first appointment to go for his consultation at the private hospital. His doctor there was called Mark; he spent two sessions, nearly 3 hours listening to Rex understanding the whole problem so he could decide how to treat him, what therapy to offer, it was costing 120 pound per session and he'd probably need ten sessions. I got back in touch with SSAFA and they said they would try to help out with the cost; I signed the consent form praying they would come up with the dosh. I didn't have the money to pay for it, but the account was in my name so it would be me they'd chase for money if none came in from the charity. Our GP could have paid for it but he had made it clear in his referral that his practice wouldn't be paying.

Rex needed treatment so what could I do when they sent me the first invoice for the assessment; 250 quid. I passed it on to SSAFA and they paid it, I hoped it would carry on like that they said they would keep paying them as long as they could.

Dave was going to be at home with his dad whilst I was at work, it was the summer break, he could look after himself but we felt like we needed to just keep an eye on him for a bit longer.

I was supposed to go back part-time but the problems had piled up whilst I was away, and I needed to get stuck in to sort stuff out. I had committed to doing the job, and now I needed to be getting on with it, taking over the new services at the beginning of the year had meant a lot of change not only for me but for the whole staff team as well.

I am driven by the quality of services we provide for our clients and I had condemned a lot of the practices that were happening within my staff team; some of the staff had been quite unnerved by my actions and I had started feeling a little guilty that I had gone in, started to change stuff and then got sick; three months I had been off by this stage.

Although I wanted to go back to work I wasn't sure I was ready to, my boss was keen to get me back after a couple of phone calls, we arranged that I would come back part-time for a month or so,

The next week I worked about 25 hours rather than the 14 we'd agreed, the next week I was full time again. The Wednesday that week saw the first Rex mini crisis; looking back it was quite funny.

Before Rex had gone away to Greece he had bought Dave a Leeds Festival ticket, he had done this loads of times for many gigs over the last couple of years, booking them through a popular reputable website and never had any problems. He had got the ticket and an early entry pass, Dave and his mates were making a holiday of it this year; they had been the year before and this time they were going as early as possible to get the maximum benefit and enjoyment from the festival. Strangely the pass had turned up, but the Festival Ticket hadn't. I had told them to ring up and find out why. It's not unusual; the fest tickets are never released until a week or two before the weekend of the festival, cuts down on forgeries I should think… it was only a couple of weeks away.

My phone started ringing as I sat doing my budget planning and trying to wade through a mountain of work, as I answered I heard Rex trying to talk to me but he was hysterical; I made out the words Leeds Ticket not coming…
I asked him to put Dave on the phone, he wasn't in a much better state than his dad; he lives for music and Festival is as important to him as Christmas to Christians and Easter to Catholics…

I told Dave to calm his dad down; tea making had become a speciality of Dave's over the years. I jumped in the Jeep and flew up the motorway, more worried about the state they were in; less worried about the ticket as I knew there would still be tickets somewhere on this planet for sale for a price, the bloomin gig…

I arrived home an hour later, and they had already been pricing up tickets on Ebay… They bloody amaze me; Dave had been able to calm him down and get him back on the internet within that hour, but when Rex has a panic attack he goes off the planet for a few minutes, this had caused Dave to panic too. I stood there in my lounge not sure whether to laugh or cry.

There's no wonder my stress levels are through the roof most days, not that I always have to deal with the problem but I always have to be on hand to advise how to deal with it, it was hard work and even more so now I was back at my day job an hour away.

The ticket arrived but because it wasn't direct from the promoters Rex was convinced it wasn't real, we managed to cope with his wobble but I was very glad once the Festival started and Dave had used his ticket to get in.

They said they had emailed Rex to say there had been a digit wrong on his reservation so they couldn't take the payment so the ticket had been cancelled, of course with everything that had been happening no one had checked emails for months… We knew they were lying about the error, why had the early entry ticket been sent if there had been no payment for it… For once I didn't have the strength, time or energy to argue.

Mark, his private doctor had started his therapy and it was going well; he came home from his sessions each week feeling a little better, he was learning coping techniques and how to use mind control, positive thinking to cope, understanding the way his illness had developed would help control it in the future, he seemed to be very focused on moving forward, the only downside was that it was still hard trying to motivate him; he was still sleeping to many hours and struggling with his high doses of medication.

I smiled to myself, as I had not only been concerned about his "illness" in the last 3 months; my real worry at this stage was how the last three months had affected him. I didn't want to make a big deal of it but I was relieved when he came home and spoke to me about it; Mark had worked through it with him in one of his sessions.

Becoming so ill in Greece had scared him to death, being restrained and detained in a police station had traumatised him, the second trip to the police station had stressed him out and made him anxious again, and the stay in the swan had plunged him back into depression.

The only time he had been able to cope in the last weeks was when he had been extremely well looked after in Waterloo, they had taken time to understand his illness and they had spent time helping him to control his symptoms. It had been another traumatic event and the way Rex had developed the symptoms of his illness was generally in response to "life events" such as trauma, or in some cases extremely "happy" events could cause just as much stress but without a doubt these last few months needed dealing with.

He had been seeing our GP to get his prescriptions but the GP still wouldn't, or couldn't change his drugs, even though he was also seemed concerned about how the medication was affecting Rex on a daily basis. However without guidance from Dr Nopal he had to keep him on the same drugs, we were due to see Nopal again the next week, so Rex decided to mention it to him direct, the impact of the medication was stopping him from getting on part of his problem was a lack of motivation the medication was making it ten times worse.

Life was whipping past at a great speed, Dave had started his new college course, I was settled back in at work and Rex was surviving at home by himself.

We turned up at Dr Nopal's the following week and straight away he started talking to Rex about drink, drugs and debt again. Rex tried to get through to him that these things were not causing problems; it was the drugs they had put him on that what holding him back, lack of proper treatment. But Nopal just kept going over the same stuff, Rex asked him directly to reduce his medication and Dr Nopal reluctantly agreed to reduce one lot by the smallest amount, not a great difference but that was better than nothing, and at least it was starting to get reduced.

Rex and I both felt that he wanted Rex to be a substance abuser, that way Nopal could put off giving the treatment that Rex needed and deserved, but they were unable to provide. Making it Rex's fault he wasn't getting treated rather than there short comings…

The conversation somehow got round to driving and Dr Nopal and Andy both mentioned that Rex should have declared his stay in hospital to the DVLA, we asked questions about why this was necessary, was there any reason why they might want to take his licence of him, they couldn't give us answers but they both said he had to make the declaration and both said very clearly that it was a formality and there would be no reason for them to take his licence away from him but he needed to tell them all the same; they assured us that he wouldn't lose his licence.

We left his office worried again, now he was scared stiff of losing his licence; getting out and about in his car was his only life line. He wasn't going out a lot, managing a couple of trips to the gym and food shopping once a week, but without the car he'd be a recluse.

I was catapulted back to looking after him full time again, trying to keep him up, but things like this made life difficult for us all.

We got the form he needed to fill in that day off the internet, it is always better to work on facts with Rex; otherwise he drives himself mad with worry and speculation.

We started filling the form in, having read all of the information provided with the form it looked like the only thing he needed to declare was his medication and doses; so we carefully wrote it all down and we included the information from Nopal he had confirmed that this was at a safe level, and stable enough to not affect his driving. He had been on the stuff for about three months now, and the enclosed leaflet said that side affects may cause problems in the first couple of weeks. For the 19 years he has had a licence; he has had one speeding ticket; and that was only about a year ago on the motorway, speeding back from his mother's… It was the middle of the night and he was doing 85 on an empty motorway, again as driving offences go I think it was a lesser "crime".

We sent it off and waited; I had almost forgotten about it as I sat in the hairdressers one Saturday morning early in October, my head was covered in foils as I was getting my hair coloured. The phone rang again and hysterical mumblings came down the line, this time I made out the words; licence gone for 3 years...

I got him to wake Dave up, and again instructed the kid to do the tea and calming down bit again, just until I could get home, my hair was only half cooked.

Crisis number 2 was just beginning; but my hair colour comes first, and I wasn't about to leave with it half cooked for any reasons, not even the queen coming to tea would have got me out of that chair before I was "done". I couldn't calm him down because I couldn't understand what had happened I had to read the letter.

Laura and Leanne, my darling hairdressers made me a cuppa; they have known about my life, having been my hairdressers for a few years now, getting my hair done has been my sanctuary my whole life, they finished my hair and I set off for home. I don't treat myself much but the hairdressers every six weeks is my one unbreakable treat.

When I got home I was shocked to read that the reason they had given for taking for his licence was that his Medication would affect his driving... I wondered where they had got that information from, it was Saturday so I could not get hold of Andy or Dr Nopal, and it would have to wait till Monday. Stress again and Dave's Birthday was just around the corner, things just seemed to keep going backwards. Unfortunately for Rex it was mostly when the Local Authorities, or their "employees made mistakes" and I was sure this was just another mistake by one of them. I think Rex knew that too, but suffering from anxiety and stress it pushed him near to the edge of mental ill health again.

My second thought came and that was that Nopal and Andy had told us lies to get Rex to make his declaration, I'd believe that Nopal might have lied, he was a prize prat, but to be fair Andy was trying to do a good job. I come across Andy's at work all the time, Social workers or Community Mental Health Nurses with massive case loads of people like Rex; people who have been detained under the Mental Health

Act that the authorities have a "responsibility" to look after. Being monitored because there is no treatment available for them.

Again I wonder what it would be like for a Macmillan Nurse trying to look after someone with cancer with out chemotherapy or radiotherapy being available.

Andy probably looks after people on a revolving door service, them going into hospital, Andy picking them up like he did Rex at the end of a stay in hospital and trying to keep them stable, extremely ill people with a half an hour visit from him each week to keep them well. If it hadn't been for me and Dave in the last few weeks I think Rex would have ended up back in hospital without a doubt, what they offered as treatment was NOTHING. Andy was a man trying to look after people with his arms tied behind his back; I struggle to think of a more soul-destroying job, joining a profession to care for people but with no chance of ever really helping them.

We had family round for Sunday dinner; that distracted him a bit but he was extremely anxious and I could see him getting in a pickle if we didn't get it sorted.

First thing Monday I was straight on the phone to Andy, asking where the DVLA had got the information about his medication from, he quickly blamed the DVLA. I told him we needed to make sure that they had been given the right doses and medications by who ever had filled in the information that had been requested from Dr Nopal.

I had good reason to mistrust the quality of services provided by our local hospital, I said it was just as a precaution, covering all angles, we had already filled in the appeal form sent by DVLA, and Andy said he'd look into it and get back to us. He did try to help us out when I got pushy, but why should I have to fight to get Rex the right help or sort out the problems they caused?

He rang back a little while later and said that he had managed to get an emergency appointment with Nopal on Friday, to go through the information that had been shared with this third party.

Data protection is very important, especially if people were sharing information about patients; they needed to be extremely careful to ensure that it was correct and accurate at the very least.

Nopal opened Rex's file and starting looking through the copy of the form that had been returned to DVLA. He said he had written this and that and then his face changed as he realised when he had got to the tick box questions; he'd ticked all the wrong ones - that's where the mistake was; he'd ticked yes instead of no to the direct question about his medication affecting his driving. This was all caused by a mistake by him, I wanted to jump up and strangle the prat.

He was lucky that Andy was there as I probably would have done, had there been no witnesses to my "crime". By this stage even Andy had the decency to blush at the enormity of this mistake, and the impact it was having on us. Since we were in Nopal's office I decided to mention the fact they had still hadn't offered anything to help except drug therapy. I raised my concerns and the next week Andy organised for Rex to go to group therapy sessions; they'd be running for 10 weeks addressing Anxiety/Stress Management. I wanted to laugh; if they stopped stressing him out he wouldn't be bloody anxious.

It was going to cost him four pounds to park every week so going on the course was actually going to cost forty quid, for some one on benefits four quid a week is a lot of money; this would cause more problems.

It would get him out of the house for a couple more hours every week, which was a good thing at least.

The private treatment was making a big difference; we were talking about him getting better again; this was the first time since he went in to Swan that we had been able to focus back on getting to the bottom of the real issue, addressing all the symptoms of his PTSD, getting him to a point where he can live with his illness without the need for high doses of prescription drugs.

That would be the best option for him and then we could start to work on sorting out the long term effects of this illness on our family.

On Dave's seventeenth birthday he had a few mates round, Rex took me into town for dinner, and life was bearable. He had stopped driving and was getting around by bus; well he'd used it twice to get into town…
He'd occasionally driven with me in the car, I had two glasses of wine that night so he'd driven home, he shook all the way; petrified the police would stop him.
They had made him give his licence back, even though Nopal had promised to send a letter to them explaining HIS mistake but the DVLA had their rules, and it didn't matter that it was a consultant's mistake…
A similar thing had happened to another friend earlier on the year after he had a seizure, but his was only for a year… I began to think they pick on people with clean driving records to keep their targets and statistics up…. Compensating for the thousands of people they can't deal with driving without licences…Driving on illegal drugs…

He was trying to be positive but he was still worried that he'd given up his job; the means to support himself and contribute to his family and all because this illness had become so debilitating. It was hard work still keeping him going but since he'd started his therapy with Mark; his "Positive Mind" was taking control, he started to take control of his life. Thinking about doing some voluntary work to get him back in the workplace, all we needed to do was sort out his pension so that could top up his income enough for him to stop worrying. I was constantly ringing and contacting the Veterans agency but they just kept fobbing me off.

At work I had problems too; I had been suspicious of some of the people I was working with now. I thought I had uncovered bad practice and needed to deal with it. I was just about coping emotionally, I earn good money to manage public funded services so I started challenging people within my team; a few people had that rabbit in headlight look; you know that startled, shit I have been caught, sort of look…

And after I asked them to explain why they refused to stop doing what they had been doing they reacted by going off sick. My anger and frustration kept me going, people who had been caught out after plenty of warning to stop and now they were pretending to be sick to avoid taking responsibility for their behaviour. I am not going to name people but they'll read this book and know who they were and was what I least needed after not long returning to work after three months of a serious stress related problem; they made my work life hell.

It is a good job I don't have the energy to hold grudges…

Good news at home though, my persistence and badgering had paid off; the wrongly revoked licence had been returned. About bloody time an all.

It is those days when you have a little victory that you have to allow yourself a pat on the back; it was a good day.

It was time to start getting ready for Christmas; I was running around like a mad woman, fitting in about seventy hours at work, half of which is "voluntary". I'm a union representative within our organisation, I was representing several people who were in various stages of the disciplinary process at work, one of whom was six months pregnant… and needed a lot of support.

I am a good manager, who tries to do a good job; I am well liked and respected within my workplace and with the Agencies that we work with. But now one of the cheeky sods off sick avoiding responsibility since I had caught them out had the front to put in a complaint about me…

They were claiming that I had bullied them, confused them and tried to run the service into the ground… I wanted to laugh; I had more than proved myself, earned myself a lot of respect, had a pile of evidence against them, but they were trying to accuse me of this. I have worked closely with about two hundred people over the last five years, never having any issues; I knew what they were doing and so did other people, but they were playing a game and I was going to be investigated.

It was a good job the day one of the two people involved had got in my face and threatened me in my office; I still remember the words clearly "that they were going to complain about me if I continued to try and stop them, excuse my language as I quote "pissing on chips" was mentioned. I'd spoken to my boss about it; I wasn't going to be threatened by anyone and it was a few days later after taking her advice that I challenged him over what he had said to me that day, that's when he developed stress and went home sick. I remembered the day; Dave's Birthday. It was a Wednesday, slap bang in the middle of the lost driving licence saga.

Now I was being investigated at work; hey ho like I didn't have enough on my plate, no staff at work, no money, energy or respite from a cruel world at home. Christmas around the corner, and now I have Cagney and Lacey on my case at work.

No time for doom and gloom, amazingly for me I had just about completed my shopping for Christmas, and was trying to get organised. It had normally been a stressful time as I have mentioned, and I tried to plan it to perfection for a stress-free week, if we got to New Years Eve with no problems I knew he would be fine. After all the years I could read him and his illness like a book… I had started writing this too; I was determined to tell my story about what's happened for many reasons.

Dawn, my sister, is moving house at the minute, I went up there yesterday to scrounge some old photos; she is having a mid-life clear out, namely if it hasn't got a use or a purpose it is going. I started to remember my earliest years; one of the things Rex has always taken the mickey out of the fact that we must have been posh; when I was a kid because we had a colour telly. They only had black and white… I'm not sure about the posh bit; we had to feed coins into the back of it every few hours.

I remember watching many things; Jesus of Nazareth, every year for about seven we had to have a pile of coins for that epic. It's about three days long!! Maybe that's an exaggeration but it felt like it, at

211

four, five, six, and so on, years of age... Once aged seven or eight I was brave enough to make our Mandy laugh during it, and she was sent to bed...I never did that again, at least with her next to me to nip, it made it go a bit quicker. The King and I and Jason and The Argonauts also amongst our Christmas favourites; Top of The Pops and a sherry with the Queen at 3pm on the dot; set your clock by the Queen on Christmas Day.

Saturday teatime was my favourite; every variety show known to man. Opportunity Knocks is the first one I think I can remember, Jim'll fix it was a favourite too. We'd talk about imaginary fix its all week at school; the real ones were never as exciting as the ones we dreamt up... The other thing we had to do was the pools; you know what I mean, no score draws and all that stuff. Saturday teatimes, I loved them...

I once wrote to Jim to ask him to fix it for me to read out the final scores so I could make someone rich... Hopefully my family, it was the late seventies and money was short for everyone, we weren't poor but everyone wanted to win the pools.
I didn't realise it was the football results until I was about 11. I'm glad Jim never fixed it for me; can you imagine if that turned out to be your fifteen minutes of fame... Shameful. I thought it was like bingo, my mothers other little addiction being in a chair meant she didn't get out that much; an occasional trip to the pub on a summers' evening when she could sit out in her chair; access rights for disabled people weren't an issue back then so getting her into places could be difficult. Dawn once left her sat outside a shop about half a mile from home and she didn't realise till she got all the way home, she had no choice but to drop the shopping and run all the way back there to rescue her. We laughed about it for years, the shop opened up onto two streets, she had left her sat at the front and sauntered out of the back...

So doing the pools was an exciting event; I suppose years later it was surpassed by the lottery. Back then in the early eighties The Sun newspaper started to play at home bingo; perfect for a housebound woman's dodgy ticker... We had to get up to go for her Saturday Sun at six in the morning as soon as the shop opened, convinced she was going to win just about every week; she and thousands of others would be waiting for one number. I once had a serious accident rushing for the said newspaper, on a brand spanking new folding ladies shopping bike, purchased by my drunk daddy from an advert in the Sunday paper; put together by my half cut Scottish brother in law, Tony. It folded in half as the peddle snapped off catapulting me across the main road at six in the morning, luckily in those days there wasn't much traffic, so I survived. As I got in, bruised, battered and bleeding all I remember is her asking for the paper. I couldn't believe it my first near death event and she didn't bat an eyelid; the bingo was more important. By that time Saturday night viewing had turned into game shows and Dallas... The "Look What You Could Have Won" days had begun; Saturday night telly started to die in my eyes.

The other thing I remembered from early on; once a year was Remembrance Sunday. I remembered being made to be quiet for what seemed like ages on Remembrance Day, watching soldiers on the telly and the Bright Red Poppies... My Grandad and uncles had been killed in the Second World War; my mum had to remember and she taught us it was important too. My Brother was in the Army and throughout my life it has remained important; a day when my husband always went to church, no matter where he was in the world.

Colour telly was best for somethings but not others, early year Jesus of N had been replaced by events like our old Nana stomping up the street for the Snooker finals, she watched in black and white until the final; it was like a treat, for her maybe, the rest of us would flee the house!

So I want to tell the story for Rex and his black and white telly years. He has always made me laugh with this jibe in particular due to some of the memories it has opened up. If I do make a bit, I might get him the plasma screen he would love... For Remembrance and respect of all the soldiers who may have, or suffered from this illness, and raise the awareness of their plight. And if I'm honest, to shame the people who failed to look after him. I think mental health; good and bad should take a much higher priority in local health services. Just like all the other illnesses that limit life in the way this has done, not only for Rex but our family too.

I thought writing it would be therapeutic; but it is much harder work than you think, carrying it all in your head whilst finding time to write it down.

The week between Christmas, I had a disciplinary hearing at work to go to. It was disgusting that someone had organised that, the person had been waiting nearly four months for resolution of this issue and now they had to sort it out at this time of year; midweek worry all over Christmas and misery for the new year, poor Julie was only weeks from giving birth. They couldn't even wait a week or fit it in before Christmas because the people who needed to be involved had been busy working half days to sort out their Christmas shopping; sometimes work makes my blood boil.

I hadn't been able to book any annual leave over Christmas as too many managers in our area had got in first, so when in the few days before Christmas an argument started over the on call service at work, I ended up having to take the on call service over New Years Eve and Day, my plans to stay sober and in control over Christmas, then to get legless on New Years Day out of the window, I was completely pissed off… Excuse my French again.

Covering a massive area from forty miles away meant no drinking or chilling out for me, and in between I had Boxing Day; the worst day of the year in our house, and then the hearing; at this rate the New Year wouldn't be starting any better or differently than the last few had. Not that getting drunk is the answer, but I am beginning to think that I am due a blow out…

I am pleased to say it was actually quite a nice Christmas; we went to our family gathering on Boxing Day, and he did his usual 'I won't drink' routine and then did, but this year he only had about 3 pints; in the past it would have been several pints and at least half a bottle of Bacardi, but for the last few years he has mostly not touched a drop. This was no problem; in fact he was extremely chilled. The medication was definitely keeping him calm. Most of our family noticed that day and I had to listen to people asking when they would start to reduce it, so we could see some of the old Rex; he had always been the life and soul of any party and now it was all he could do to manage to stay awake after 8pm. After a pleasant day I drove us home and he slept…

A 200% improvement on the last seven or eight boxing days, Christmas has seen major manic periods fuelled by too much booze, bless the family party. The medication had helped but they still hadn't reduced it enough to stop the oversleeping problems. His positive mind therapy had given him the willpower to make himself drink slower and control himself; it was a shame the medication made him appear over medicated; everyone was noticing and that was starting to limit his life, and his ability to move on from the intense period of illness he had suffered.

I went through the motions at work that week. I couldn't help but get angry and upset by having to support Julie through her hearing at work; it was very stressful and I just felt helpless, it had been badly organised for Christmas week but in another way it was good to be getting it over and done with. She had this cloud over her head for months, but it was hard keeping myself upbeat by that stage, so giving energy to others as much as I don't mind on a normal day, by this time it was draining my own very tight reserve energy tank.

It was on the very same day that my administrator decided to ring me in hysterics due to a ghost haunting her at work in our office fifteen miles away, I wasn't sure what she wanted me to do as she babbled her way through ringing bells and spooky feelings.
I tried not to laugh; I had never heard about any haunting in the building and I am normally quite in tune with the spirits, it doesn't look like an old building; it's cladded in that corrugated aluminium stuff. But we know it was the old cinema. I wondered if it had anything to do with that.

I told her to lock up and go home, I couldn't do anything else.

I have noticed over the last few years on the work front it has got quieter and quieter, with more people planning longer breaks over the festive break; travelling in rush hour makes you notice these things and travelling in a soft top jeep makes the weather important too, and to be fair the weather has been extremely mild for the last few years too.

Quiet sunny trips to work had become the "norm" for travelling over the festive period.

So she went home to enjoy the holidays with most other people in this country; not many people were at work at all, so one less wouldn't make a big difference.

We got a fair hearing and Ju was going off on leave to have her baby. I was smiling by the end of the day, I had done as good a job as possible for the organisation and that always made me happy.

I am good at my job and thinking back over the last few years it had probably kept me sane. Days like this when things go right after months of working on supporting Julie and knowing she can now sort her problems out at last makes me smile, a ghost in my office scaring staff was the least of my worries.

Surviving Christmas facing forward

January is starting and there was no major crisis other than the haunting to report. The money for the private therapy has dried up, only enough for one emergency session is left but Mark has told Rex he will be ok; he has taught Rex that mental health is dependant on your "Positive Mind" staying in control.

That was the best way to control the symptoms of his illness "Mind over Matter". Anxiety, depression, stress, any of the labels they give your mental ill health can be controlled like this if you can just afford the on going treatment; you need to help you help yourself, because at the end of the day it's not like a broken bone where they can measure the results of "physiotherapy" that has kicked in after your plaster cast has come off. With mental health you can get therapy, but the home exercises are very important; only you can sort out your thoughts. The good and the bad ones. Mark had been able to teach Rex this, now Rex had to carry on. I was a little concerned about the treatment ending, but I had to be cool about it as I didn't want Rex to worry; if I worried he worried that's the way it works.

Rex was trying to keep going but still no news of his pension; coupled with the fact that he is used to spending loads at Christmas this year he'd had a miniscule budget and he was skint, this had lead to him getting a little low after Christmas. It was getting harder to keep positive, and I was getting pissed off that at this stage, when all he needed was some financial help, we were involved in a lengthy process of applying for his pension. I think he should be entitled to his pension if he had been looked after by the Government when he left the forces he would never have got into this state…

Just his pension and some more interaction from the NHS to get more therapy leading to a reduction in his medication would help loads with his recovery, allowing for him to start to move forward with his life.

Reality was that they just wanted to keep him medicated so he didn't end up back in hospital, but they had no idea of what they should be doing to treat him because as I sit here writing this it is just over a year since I busted him out of that shit hole, and he has still had no offer of therapy.

Nobody in our health service has even discussed his PTSD with him, even though it is clear he has got it.

Using high levels of mood stabilising medication wasn't the answer; that's just a bog standard approach to mental health care. I'd liken it to giving someone paracetamol for a migraine, it might provide short term relief but it won't get rid of the problem.

The excellent team in Waterloo could see that he had more than the manic episode which is what his consultant was still treating him for. Our GP has known about his illness for at least five years, he had coped for the last three months with the help of his private therapist being treated for PTSD…

I can't help thinking it's strange that it was at Nopal's clinic, four years ago that this illness Post Traumatic Stress was suggested as a diagnosis for Rex's illness; yet Nopal was insistent on treating him for the small manic episode. From the appointments I had attended since he had left hospital it seemed that despite what Rex said he insisted on thinking of Rex as a druggie, with drink and money problems, he might get away with that with some people but not my husband.

I still felt that, after suffering sunstroke and a physical attack in Greece last year he had had a complete breakdown. I had known him long enough, the lovely kind friends that looked after him in Crete state a few beers and a single shared spliff had been all he had in the weeks leading up to him "losing the plot"; evidently not causing the problem that was down to his already unstable mental health; had obviously been pushed over the edge by the attack and sunstroke.

Nopal wouldn't listen; he probably had lower "targets" for treating people with "substance abuse issues". Possibly the more patients he diagnosed with that, the less he needed evidence, they could get on waiting lists for rehab…

That's fifteen months up to now that he has waited for appropriate treatment since he entered the Mental Health Services full time, as I'd call it; since he had his breakdown last year and five years since he first went to our GP for help. Drug therapy is cheap and easy to monitor if someone has got a fulltime carer; namely me and Dave. But why should we look after him forever, nobody should have to be dependant on someone else unless they have to be and with treatment and therapy he could be doing well.

Andy was still popping in once in a while to make sure that Rex was still getting by; he had got him on a computer course to try and fill a couple of hours a week replacing the time he had been going out to his anxiety group, now that had finished this was Andy's attempt to keep him "busy".

The funny thing was me and Dave were managing to keep Rex's spirits up by laughing with him as he described; how anxious people in the group had been and how they had all missed the group at some stage because they had been too stressed and anxious to get there. Rex had missed a week when he lost his licence, but we managed to calm him down for the next week.

I do believe he was one of only two people who managed to miss one group; he is desperate to get any treatment that will help him combat this illness.
This confirmed my belief that he would never have refused treatment since his return; if he had been looked after properly. It still makes me angry about the way he had been looked after by our local hospital.
I knew without a doubt that it had caused him more distress than was ever needed; the scars on his wrists from the handcuffs were still quite an angry red colour, a physical reminder for him of what had happened…

Locking up mad people in police cells in this day and age is barbaric; they may as well have chained him to the wall like they used to a hundred years ago. Their treatment had been disgusting and I made up my mind that the people who had abused my husband and nearly broken my family would apologise for what they'd done.

I want to make sure that he made a stand against a health authority who clearly feels this is a good way to treat mad people; I have evidence that it happens all the time and they get away with it. It has to stop.

Another ex soldier, a really young guy battling with the same illness in our area has been on the front page of our local newspaper a few times. The last time for having also had an encounter with the armed response unit, he ended up pinned to the middle of a road with several guns pointing in his face.

I know that should make me feel better; that we aren't the only people going through this, but all I could feel was extreme empathy for his dad and the rest of his family. I know his Dad; I have met him a few times through one of the charities I have contacted in the last year.

I can't decide how to feel but I know it breaks my heart, as I have started to look into government statistics for several things including PTSD and soldiers who are AWOL; I can only ever function and keep my life going forward if I base my life on fact, it is the only way to work.

I am constantly keeping up with changes to the law in relation to Housing, Mental Health Offending Behaviour and Government Funding for the charity I work for, so looking for information related to this was a doddle. Lots of website and information available finding out about PTSD was much easier than living with it as an uninvited guest into your family.

The evidence I have seen indicates there's a big group of people like Rex in this country, not a forgotten platoon or squadron. I think it is probably nearing the size of a forgotten Army.

I got through January thinking how I could try and uncover how big this problem is in this country and exposing the failure of the Government but it had to be a battle for another day.

I rang the solicitor to find out what she thought about the information I had sent to her; she had spoken to a barrister who thought that he had a strong case for medical negligence.

I do wonder how long the waiting list for treatment will be; I don't want to monitor someone's medication for the rest of my life; that's the easiest option for the health service. I want my husband well again. It was around this time my friend Sue stopped me in my tracks at work by suggesting that I should forget the old Rex and enjoy the new one. To be honest to myself I have to admit there were some bits of the new one that were starting to drive me mad; sleeping till lunch time for one, he has always worked and been active; playing squash and golf, now all he did was sleep, go out to his computer class and shopping.

The depression was creeping back in; bought on rapidly by a guilty feeling as I had stepped up the pressure on the kid to get a job. Fortunately for him he has never had to work because we have always had enough money for most things, but it is running out fast and I am getting stressed again.

Rex isn't anywhere near ready to go back to work; but it doesn't stop him from feeling guilty that I am still running the same house and bills on a lot less money, and he can't even afford to treat himself to new pants let alone treat the kid like he always had with a tenner for the cinema here, and twenty quid for a gig there; his mood was sinking.

Then we got the news that he had been turned down for his pension because he was a drug addict; who had made life choices to abuse drugs. Guess who had given them that information? They'd picked up on the trace of cannabis in his urine on his return from Greece and added that to Nopal's reports that have him down as a substance abuser and his claims that he was a drug baron during his few psychotic days, were in a report somewhere and had been quoted…
I didn't know whether to laugh or cry at the ridiculous stuff they had concluded after the last seven months of investigating Rex's illness; I think I can honestly say I laughed right up to the point that I remembered

that it would mean loads of work to appeal it... I have a job besides looking after him remember.

I wrote his appeal based on the fact that he had also claimed he was a Greek God, but he now realised he wasn't. There was absolutely no evidence of heavy, prolonged use of drugs anywhere in his medical documents or history, because it has never been the problem; they hadn't mentioned the well documented abuse of alcohol...

Could that be because the army condone heavy drinking so probably wouldn't want to accept it as an addiction or problem attached to mental health problems after the army? That "symptom" of his illness had definitely started in the last year of his army life was alcohol abuse, but because we lived apart with him in Ireland, and me and Dave in England, his time at home as I said was "holidays" for him; it hadn't been a major problem but it had started back then.

I wasn't going to accept this decision; it was wrong. A few spliffs over the years maybe wrong to some people, but acceptable to others; no different to "binge drinking" in the fact that they are both bad for you, it's just one's legal and the other isn't.
Well that's my opinion and it is my book and I would make sure it wasn't going to give them an excuse not to pay him his dues...

When I contacted the Veterans Agency they more or less told me that it was normal for claims to be turned down for ridiculous reasons and that most claims had to go to appeal. How can that be acceptable when not only Rex but probably many others will be suffering stress and anxiety about money whilst they get caught up in a bureaucratic mess that calls itself a support service for service personnel. They indicated it could take up to two years to get Rex any money. I said they needed to sort themselves out; the only saving grace was that his "welfare officer" for the agency had been a help a good ear to bend over the months.

I stopped holding my breath; still no money for him or good support but no point stressing too much.

February Again

I have learnt to expect doom and gloom in February; so this year, being a firm believer in changing things, I decided that it would be better or that I would die before my birthday in March trying to make it better.

Dave was doing well at college, so that was something positive, and my birthday was just around the corner. Things seemed to be going well; no major events to report on the home front; mostly things just ticked on. Rex was getting more depressed by the day but me and Dave, and some family members and friends worked hard to keep him going. He had started having panic attacks again, and there seemed to be a lot of anxiety but his mood was still stable thanks to the ever provided medication. The other symptoms were slowly coming back though, I kept reminding him that he had to keep going with his positive thoughts and focusing on having good days, but with not too much to do with his time, it was still easier to sleep most of the day away.

At work the people who had complained about me were still off sick, but somehow as a team we seemed to be moving forward; things were a lot happier than they had been in months, and I didn't mind being there for the first time in ages; I was really starting to enjoy my job again.

One afternoon I was sat in the office by myself, since the "haunting of the administrator" had occurred over the Christmas period it came to light that we did have an alleged spook; the old projectionist from the cinema days had been known to be around in the building.

We hadn't spoken about it for ages, and I certainly wasn't consciously thinking about it as I was sat talking to someone on the phone. The fire door outside my office slammed shut it; was strange because it is pinned open all day, as it is the only route to the kettle and it needs to be open…Health and Safety I know state that fire doors shouldn't be pinned open, but there's only the kitchen beyond it…

The access to the kettle needs to be quick; sometimes the need for caffeine is so strong. I carried on talking and it slammed again, thinking someone must be in the office. I stopped the conversation for a minute to check who was in, someone had to be doing it, once the door is shut you have to press the door handle to open it, it can't reopen itself, spooky.

No one was in the corridor, or the offices and the door was still pinned open. Bemused I sat back down and carried on talking, it happened again. I won't get all dramatic and "Most Haunted" on you but it went on for nearly thirty minutes; Deb and Nicola, two of the support workers returned to the office and it stopped immediately. They laughed a lot about the state I was in as they went and made me hot, sweet tea for my visible signs of shock.
I am not normally spooked but this was strange; the way it started and stopped, and it was aggressive banging, not the little taps you'd normally associate with haunting; it had shocked me.

I got on about my business and a few days later I was working from home when my work phone rang; it was Nicola calling from the office accusing me of stealing half a flake; me her trusted, wonderful boss branded a chocolate thief… I had seen it in her lunch box the day before but I had not bloomin stolen it, I would have left an I.O.U if I had taken it, but I was the last person out of the office so I was getting the blame. I swear I didn't take it, but it had gone, and the wrapper had been put back in the lunch box.

After fifteen minutes debating the likelihood of me stealing chocolate we agreed if it wasn't me, it had to be the ghost, and after a twenty minute call I think she believed me; I can put my hand on my heart and say I didn't steal it.

I chuckled to myself the next day when I went over to our local church; they have a small coffee shop, and it is right next to our office so we all use it for lunch most days, we know them all and they know us. Fabulous sandwiches, Dawn doesn't even need to ask for she knows us so well.

As I stood waiting for my sandwich the local vicar sidled up to me having over heard people talking about our spooky occurrence, namely the missing flake episode, not the day I was freaked out, after a small chat he offered his ghost busting services.

I declined and left clutching my sandwich, hoping that this would be the end of the haunting. I didn't want to find out what paperwork is needed to get an Exorcism in our office, our organisation is extremely risk averse so anything out of the ordinary generates a massive amount of paperwork, as you can imagine.

The month closes and my birthday arrives; it's a very pleasant day. I was at work, and they had bought me chocolate cake for breakfast...Luxury.
I had leftover chocolate cake for lunch, and then when I got home, Rex and Dave were waiting with guess what? Yes, chocolate cake.
Since I turned twenty five I have never let birthdays or getting older upset me. I think it's a process to be cherished; me growing up (I am nearly there at 38) means I get to see my son turning into a man I am proud of. I can get him to drive me around for a change!
I can look back on my fashion tastes and haircuts and laugh; I have lots of memories to make me smile. I have watched the world changing around me, not all for the better as we well know. The most amazing fact is that I look much younger than I did in the eighties, like many of my friends. That's why I like my birthday; it grounds me and reminds me what I have to live for. I do enjoy life; there's something to smile or laugh about most days.

Even February hadn't beaten me this year; I was feeling fine, yet for the last six years I have hated my birthday. It has just reminded me that my Dad was buried the day before it. This year I enjoyed it for a change.
I miss my Dad at odd times now; like when something comes on, an old seventies show or a song, nicer memories instead of being fixated with the fact that he had died. I supposed bereavement takes different amounts of time for different people, but for me it seems to have passed

now. Maybe that has something to do with the calm Rex we live with; since his breakdown last year he has been so much easier to live with; the illness is now under control of a sort and life's a lot calmer for us all.

Strangely, I don't remember grieving for my mum, but I suppose at thirteen I wasn't in control of my thoughts, that evil adolescence had hold of me at the same time and sometimes looking back on my outrageous teenage years, where I did all the usual sulking, drinking, swearing, fighting and arguing with anyone who stood in my way sorts of thing. It's hard to separate or understand what was normal teenage stuff and what was caused by my bereavement but I don't dwell on that I try to look forward. I suppose I was angry for a couple of years.

Nopal
Definition: worst consultant psychiatrist a person could ask for...

Thanks to some sort of minor miracle; or maybe in response to my many prayers he is retiring, Rex is to see him one more time, then never again; thank god. The session was the same as all the rest, a waste of time.

Rex had been promised a reduction of medication at the last appointment; the over sleeping was causing a lot of problems. Nopal had said all along that after nine months of "stable" mental health, the medication would be reviewed; now nine months had passed, he refused to do it because he wanted Rex to wait and meet his new consultant.
I wanted to scream but it wouldn't get us anywhere after years of giving Rex no treatment, bad advice, and losing him his driving licence. I wasn't going to miss Nopal and I was sure Rex wouldn't either; maybe the new guy that was coming in would be better.

Don't get me wrong Nopal was always pleasant and smiley. I just wish he could have helped Rex a bit more, but for Rex and me trying to get him to understand what the problem really was had been too much hard work, and he still hadn't spoken to Rex about PTSD; despite the consultants at both Waterloo and Swan being convinced that was what was wrong with him, as well as our own GP having the opinion that he had suffered from PTSD since leaving the army; Nopal was never going to treat him for it or admit that he has it.

Rex had told him several times about it all over the last four years, but still no help, just an intense drug treatment that is usually used to keep psychotic people calm and stable. Understanding the symptoms of mental health I don't think he was truly psychotic; he presented more neurotic last May to me. I am not sure why he had refused to talk about Rex's real problems, I can only assume that he hadn't read the reports from the other hospitals or listened to anything that Rex had ever said, so we'd have to hope for the best from the new guy.

Well something more than cannabis is the problem, and go to relate which was all he'd ever got from Nopal.

My sister had been nagging me to go on holiday; we had said ages ago that we would have a week in Greece together; now she was at me to get something booked. I started to look for flights and a friend of ours in Greece contacted us to say that there was a job for Rex if he felt well enough to go back out there. They had been asking about him and keeping up with how he was doing through my brother mainly; but they loved him and they wanted him back. They knew that he was a good person; they had all been so worried about him the year before; they were desperate to see him.

Rex couldn't decide whether to go or not, so I decided I would get him a ticket for his birthday; that way he could go for a week with us all, see everyone. I knew he was worried about going back but I knew there was no need for worry; if he wanted to stay he could go back out later on once the job was to start.

Dave was to stay at home by himself; at seventeen and a half he refused to go stay with anyone like he had in the past. I knew he would be safe and sensible but I was worried about parties... Who wouldn't? We have all been teenagers. I had mates climbing out the back window as my sister and her husband came through the front door in my hay day, it was a mid terraced house, my mates had to fight through gardens for freedom...

By the first week in April we are on our way; my brother has driven down, he always goes for Easter to the Greeks; it is the main celebration of the year and he likes to be there.

Before I even get on the plane I am checking that Dave is ok, there are a few people keeping an eye on him; but there's no harm in checking is there?

We arrive and I can't believe how pleased everyone is to see us, much to my surprise even our Greek male friends are kissing Rex; a sign of great affection... I was so pleased. I knew he was worried that they would all think badly of him from what had happened the year before in his "madness", but they didn't care about that, they just wanted to know he was ok now, and he was getting better except the sleeping. It didn't take long for them to notice the changes though, my brother said he has lost his bottle, I think that's true to some extent; he has lost his bottle to live, scared of anything going wrong that might cause him stress again. He hates being over medicated but he is also a little scared of coming off of it for that reason he doesn't want to go backwards but he was slow at moving forward.

We had a lovely week and all too soon we were on the flight home; and for a change it was raining. The job was on offer but I wasn't sure he was ready to go anywhere yet; Rex was trying to be optimistic that this time it could work, I vowed to be there for him whatever.

He was working hard to complete his computer course in case he decided to take the job in Greece.

I contacted the Veterans agency again; we hadn't heard anything since January when we had put in the appeal against their decision not to award Rex a pension.

Helen, his worker from the agency agreed to go out and see him by herself, I was fed up with having to sort everything out and she agreed to try and get him to deal with his pension claim himself.

Within the week she had been out to see him, talking to him about his Greek plans. She told him scary things about what would happen with his benefits and pension if he went abroad to live/work...
By the time I got home from work that day he was having a panic attack; and could hardly control himself. Rex wanted to work and provide for himself, he wanted a life back, and Greece could be an option. He didn't have to make a snap decision; the job wasn't going to start for a few weeks yet but from what she'd said he'd gone into stress mode and it would take weeks to calm him down again. He wouldn't need to worry about benefits if he could try to be well enough to work.
His little glimmer of optimism about moving his life forward came to an abrupt stand still again; he started getting extremely depressed, we had days of crying and little panic attacks.

I suggested he go to see our GP to get some anti depressants to help lift his mood again, but he was convinced he wanted less medication not more. I tried several times to explain that different medication works on different things but he still didn't want more medication. He was depressed again; he needed anti depressants for sure; life was getting a little stressful with him again.
Most of my free hours outside of work were spent in one to one support sessions with my so called husband, he was starting to feel like my own private patient and I resented the health services for leaving me to look after him the way they had. The Veterans agency and Combat Stress had helped a little but not enough to take on some of the burden of looking after someone so ill or so skint...

I went to a meeting at The Veterans agency in March; I met one of those people who say show stopping things to you. This one had blown me away. It was still playing on my mind some weeks later, a guy who has a good job, doing good work with people with poor mental health and knows a lot about "Combat stress" had listened to what we had all said in relation to the effects the illness had on us individually. The mix of people in the meeting was that some had the illness; some of them were "carers" like me. Having described some of the things I had been through with Rex and debating with the guy in question how far you go to look after loved ones he suggested that I was acting like a Martyr.

Just because it bugged me putting it down in my book will remind me to go back and talk to him again; he was just a bit judgemental I felt, but then I like that a bit sometimes; it makes you think. I can assure you all that I would never give my life up for anything. I am too important to me to give myself up, maybe I did at one stage but not for the last couple of years; I have got stronger but I still could never abandon him if that makes sense.

I think he not only hurt my feelings when he said that he made me look back on how much I had asked for help for Rex, and how much we had been through last year and still it was up to me to look after him because there was no one else, and I couldn't put him out on the street, could I?

April through to May was difficult; I had a lot going on at work and unrest at home. I was starting to feel frazzled but I had to keep going; there was too much to do at work and home to stop. He had never been good at decision making; now he had to decide if going back to Greece was the best option. I had told him the facts about his benefits and stuff but he was still worried about what Helen had said to him; he was getting desperate for something to change. He still didn't get the full picture, that he had to have things right in his own head; it didn't matter what anyone else thought, advised or said; it only mattered that it was the right choice in his head. The decision had to be made by him; that way he had to take responsibility for it. It was the therapy that had helped him out last year, positive thinking.

It was further complicated by the Veterans Agency inviting him to attend to talk to a panel of three senior people in the agency about the problems he was experiencing; trying to get the treatment for this very obvious illness. He didn't want to miss that; it might stop him from getting his pension appeal. Decisions, decisions... He asked if I would go to the panel with him and of course I said yes. I was sick of it, I had spent hours writing letters to the veterans agency, days on the phone too, as well as sorting out his debts and bank account, trying to keep it all together for him so he wouldn't stress. I was fed up but if I didn't agree to go he wouldn't agree to see them anyway.

He's been unable to work for over two years due to being so ill; he needed his pension. Living on benefits was stressing him out; that was the main reason he wanted to go to Greece to work.

Every job you go for in this country wants to know your background and your sickness record and the thought of having to tell anyone that he had been sectioned brought him out in a cold sweat.

My sister was going out to Greece for the season this year so he would have some company; someone to talk to. But he was scared of making any choices; he has convinced himself that he always makes the wrong decisions. I think it was at this point that I started to lose my patience again; I had to constantly reassure him that everything was going to be ok but I wasn't convinced it would, to be honest. I knew that getting on a flight to Greece would be the easiest decision for him to make and that would be that; until he needed me to pick up the pieces again.

I spoke to him again about seeing the GP for some anti-depressants because he was low and struggling to keep himself on an even keel. No word from the hospital, so no idea when he'd see the new consultant. It had been seven weeks since his last appointment with Nopal, and Andy had broken a limb so it was just us again. The medication hadn't been reduced and he was still sleeping fourteen hours a day sometimes; now he thought he could go and work forty hours a week in the baking heat in Greece.

I knew it was a gesture for him; it would be the easiest solution to show me he was trying to do something about himself, helping himself to get better would be the Greek option, leaving me to go to the panel alone... I knew the routine; this would be the third time he'd done it.

The only thing, is in situations like this the easiest choice always backfires because he then convinces himself that it's either going wrong, or has gone wrong, because he was forced to make the wrong choice.

This is normally blamed on someone or something else. I think its called transference; he projects his "problems" onto real things and situations to avoid dealing with the real problem; his poor mental health

Holiday

By the middle of May I was looking for flights for my sister and Rex; I knew he would decide to go and he had. I had Helen from the agency amongst others asking me if I thought he should go, but who I am to tell him what he can or can't do? I have tried everything I can think of to try to get him out and about; I have bribed him, to get him to speak to people, I have had to get them to ring on the sly. To keep him motivated I have asked him to do house stuff whilst I am at work. I have loved him and looked after him for the past twenty-one years, but I can't tell him what to do. I had said love, honour, cherish, not control, nurse and detain.

Just before the end of May he was gone; him, my sister and enough Cheddar to pull the plane out of the sky. They had both booked two weeks return; I knew I wouldn't be seeing her in two weeks, she is stubborn and I knew she would stay out there whether she liked it or not, but as I left him at my sisters waiting to go to the airport I knew he'd be back shortly (very shortly probably) on the return flight.

The next two weeks at work were going to be manic. I had two days on a course in London, quite a demanding course.
As well as meetings with local authorities over the contracts we have with them to provide services in the community. There is never a dull moment in a normal week let alone in one where days are taken out of the office; in these two weeks I think I only had three days in the office..

Then the next week I had days out learning about the government's new plans to manage offenders as well as various other things on going, issues with some of the people that I worked with so again I was always going to be busy. It was quite nice to get home to no brain strain though; no one to worry about except me and Dave, but to be fair I don't often worry about him; he is generally ok as long as I am.
He is so easy going that he just gets on with stuff he is normally busy with college and gigs.

I knew that this was just a two week break from being his full time carer so I just got on with the next two weeks expecting him back.

Within just three days of being there he had decided that he couldn't stay; he had realised he probably wasn't ready to go but he did want to work, he just wasn't well enough to look after himself yet.

I wondered if he would ever be ready to look after himself; I know that may sound harsh but as I sat starting this book it was a real worry; now I have nearly finished it I am more optimistic.

I was on the phone to him just about everyday; keeping him calm as he became hysterical on the phone, having panic attacks about what would happen to him. He was feeling very stressed out but I wasn't sure that coming home to our house would make any difference.

We would just spend more hours talking about why he thought he couldn't get a job; he was worried because he had been sectioned. First question when you get any job is "What has your sickness record been like?" I could understand his fears; we were on a roundabout with his illness. I tried hard to think of ways to stop the roundabout because the motion sickness was getting out of control.

The day before he was due back I attended the panel hearing with the Veterans Agency; the experts in looking after people like my Rex, people who have this illness and need treatment and help to get better.

I went through his whole story again; start to finish, everything in this book, in twenty minutes flat. Not the quickest I have done it in but they needed details of active duty. Pity they don't have Olympics for speed talking; I could easily go for gold it must have been about the hundredth time I had been through it. All I can remember from the day was sitting thinking how sick I was of telling this story, the story I need to convince others to read; I hope it hasn't bored you too much.

By the end of it two of the three panel members sat aghast, that the story that I had told was true; but what they didn't realise it's easy to remember stories when you have lived them; that's half the problem when looking after someone like Rex.

Writing this has been quite easy; to be honest I haven't had to make anything up.

They were stunned on several levels a) that I had stood by him through it and b) that he had been so ill for so long, without appropriate help despite having been involved with the local mental health services for a few years. They seemed keen to want to use Rex as an example of how the system is failing our veterans; despite NHS trusts being given guidance from the government on the diagnosis and treatment of illnesses triggered by time served in the forces.

After I had given them Rex's history I asked what they could do to help Rex, a reasonable question. I just wasn't prepared for the answer; they said they couldn't help because he hadn't been awarded a pension. I had told them he was in the middle of appealing the decision to not give him a pension during my recital of our life together in the last few years; a fact they should have been aware of before the invite to attend the panel had been sent. A thought passed my mind that I was pleased it was me hearing that they couldn't help and not Rex. I think being turned down for help from every avenue we tried was starting to affect him it was getting him down, the pension meant extra money and that was his major stress.

I thanked them for their time, left the building and drove around the corner again. I was sat sobbing my heart out; in the last year I have knocked on doors, contacted our local MP, phoned people from the benefits agency to charities, begged for someone to help my husband survive the illness that had started around the time just before, or as he finished in the army.

No one seemed to want to help, and I was tired of doing it. Life shouldn't be hard work. My strong belief is that work should be hard to help make life easy. Living with anyone with a debilitating illness such as Rex's is hard work as I am sure a lot of you are unfortunately aware.

I drove home feeling flat and deflated; one of the panel members spoke about a hardship pension that could be available but I wasn't sure what he said; my brain was just too full to take anymore on board. Not because I didn't want to help but because I couldn't think of anything else to do to help Rex, or get him to help himself we had both been trying.

Just to recap, this illness has been around for what feels like forever but in reality it's only a small portion of the time we have been together. I love him; he's been a good husband and my best friend but now on top of my own life stresses I had to consider him constantly; his battle for his pension, his lack of motivation and money, the lack of treatment to speed up his healing process after his breakdown last year. It still felt like I was in a nightmare with nowhere to turn. It is heartbreaking to watch someone you love be disabled like this, whether it's your husband, brother, mother or sister. It is as devastating whether it is mental health or physical health causing the problems.

On top of all that Rex had felt trapped by himself before he went back to Greece, scared to go out in case the world stresses him out, unable to work for the same reason and the over sleeping issue has now become a habit. I knew it had been developed by months of over medication all affecting the quality of his life.

I couldn't turn my back on him now even though the situation was driving me mad again; I had to keep going. One of the points I ponder about as I write this book is why can some people cope with life's stress and strains and carry on and some can't? I have been diagnosed with reactive depression; I think some people who know me would say I even get a little manic. But somehow I can get up everyday and get on; I am not alone and I am not special but I know there are more and more people giving up to the affects of "daily life".

I often do more work in two days than I do in the next three weeks; that's just the way I live but something inside me keeps control of my brain so I can keep going. The downside is the bit that stops calorie intake and things that are "bad" for me doesn't work so well, but I can live with that.

Looking back the day with the Veterans' agency had pissed me off big time but to be honest in the grand scheme of things it wasn't that big of an issue, we'd get by we always had.

The real problem was the stigma he still felt from having a mental health problem and having now been sectioned made him think he couldn't get a job or move on, I just knew it was going to be a battle to sort out.

The Veterans' agency agreed that he had PTSD but wouldn't pay his pension because he didn't see the doctor about his mental health until a couple of years after he had left the army.

I hope in this book I have explained enough to understand why it took so long for him to go; he left the army free at last, life getting better and togetherness that we had longed for; holidays and a social life that was ace. No-one close to Rex could understand why he felt like he did. That helped him convince himself that he couldn't be depressed or anxious and so on for ages, all the time it getting worse. Two twenty-minute appointments with Nopal over three years were all that had been offered.

Now two independent hospitals had also confirmed that they felt the cluster of illnesses that they had seen dominated by manic depression over the years would be described as PTSD.

Yet our hospital said they were treating him for an intense period of "psychosis" that he had suffered last year, now labelled as "Manic Depression". We had been confused by it; we both knew what we had been through and it certainly wasn't what had happened last year with his health that was the main thing; the number one problem all along was the lack of treatment over a period of years.

My husband had once been a proud soldier; he then went on to be a good provider, working hard at his job once he left the army getting a good job supporting me so I could get a better job. Life could only get better for us three but instead of us prospering, this illness had taken hold and left him in a society where binge drinking is acceptable. The early years had been scary, what with his mood swings and his anxiety, and the occasional aggressive outburst that came with alcohol and the Veterans' agency had, in a way called us both liars in refusing his pension. Why would anyone say they'd been through what he has been through in the last years if it hadn't happened? I knew he never wanted to give up work; he was too ill to carry on working. Having lived with him for many years I can testify on my life that he was never a big drinker; we both got drunk if we went out but most of the time Rex would be the first person to leave the bar after drinks on Friday afternoon, enjoying a few pints before he came home instead of staying out getting legless with his mates in the NAAFI; drinking is a big part of the Army culture. He started drinking heavily the year he finished in the army; he now thinks he knows when the depression started and that was around the same time; just as he had recovered from his ski accident and signed the paperwork for his release.

What we had thought would be a short period of wobbly mental health after a major lifestyle change; leaving the Army had turned into a six year nightmare landing us here. He was the one really suffering; him and the thousands of people probably suffering like him after their experiences in the forces. The agencies that the government say are there to help are ridiculous; looking at information on the web there are lots of campaigns; we had good support from SSAFA and the British Legion last year, the old established charities that have been around for years. The 'newer' services offered by the "Government" are crap to say the least.

It is not very often that I get stuck for ideas; I am quite a resourceful human but by now, and after many years of trying I didn't know what to do next.

Just another thought; if in "society" you get ill the government usually pay you sickness benefit until you can no longer prove that you are ill, as long as you are "sick" they will pay you something.

In the case of soldiers applying to the same government for pensions it is the opposite, you become ill they keep the money till you prove how ill you are... How is that fair?

I wanted the panel to write to the hospital to ask for some support but...

Back Again

After working all the next day I drove to the airport to pick him up. He couldn't look me in the eye; I think he was embarrassed that he was back being dependant on me for everything. He wanted to stand on his own two feet and in some ways he resents the dependency on me that this illness has created as much as I do, but he just isn't well enough to look after himself yet.

I had been worried about it for ages; it isn't healthy for someone to need someone else that much but I couldn't kick him out. I had even suggested he try to get a flat around the corner so he could look after himself with my support, but how could he get a flat when so many people with problems much worse than his are living on the street and can't get flats? What chance did he have?

We got home and he was very subdued; I could hardly get any conversation out of him, no news of friends in Greece. He had walked out of Greece not saying goodbye to anyone and over the next few days he slumped into a deep depression.

The weeks ticked by and I became more and more desperate to get him out of his depression but nothing was working. He was spending all his time at home with Dave, and things were getting strained again. When he is feeling crap like that he transfers his misery onto others and whilst Dave was trying hard to get a job, it was proving to be difficult and Rex was making the situation worse by getting in sly digs and winding him up.

No appointments had come through from the hospital to meet the new consultant so he was back to sleeping away most of the day to combat the boredom. I suppose with no help he would never get any better and like I said I was at a loss.

Working ten hours a day in a demanding, busy job and coming home to the same misery everyday was driving me mad again.

Eventually I convinced him to go back to the GP to talk about getting some anti-depressants; I couldn't live with his misery, it was getting harder and harder and even he could see that through his misery. Rex wanted me to go with him to see the GP; he always worries that they will ask him something that he doesn't know the answer to. When Rex had asked our doctor about changing his medication previously the doc had always referred him back to Nopal. I had convinced him that the GP might help since he hadn't seen anyone from the CMHT or hospital for a few weeks. I had booked a flight to go and see my sister in Greece for the beginning of July and I wanted to try and have a break; worrying about him being so depressed whilst I was away was not an option; I needed and deserved this break. I knew Dave would be able to look after his Dad, I didn't think there was any chance of a big breakdown, but it would be nice for them to have some chill-out time together whilst I was away. We booked an appointment that was a week away; the only GP Rex will see is the most popular in the practice. It took some convincing to get Rex some anti-depressants and I again left the appointment wondering why everything was such a battle. I think the GP was torn between sticking to "protocol" working with the Consultant when people have been sectioned and listening to me, the woman who hardly ever takes time to take herself to the doctors and only comes with Rex when it's really bad at home; thankfully I think he has realised that after the last few years.

He started with his new medication and I went of on my holiday much happier. There was only one panic attack whilst I was on holiday, that I am aware of, a letter from the bank or something like that. I managed to get him calm by "phone" and Dave made the tea again....

July started very nicely; quite a few family and friends had gathered for a break. One of my brother's ventures was due to get started; it made the holiday a bit hectic but in between it was hitting 45 degrees every day, and I was baking myself to a crisp; swimming and laughing at my mad nieces' antics and generally not worrying about the pressures of work or worrying about the crap at home; my brain slowed down a bit, well as much as it can when you are surrounded by lovely people

241

that you don't get to spend enough time with at home. I still didn't sleep much and I didn't proof read the chapters from this book that I took.

I didn't care though; it was a holiday, my first proper one in two years and they had been bloody hard years (I didn't count the one earlier in the year as a proper break, it had been spent running around and looking after Rex making sure he was ok with it being his first trip since the last year's events.)

I didn't want to go home as I sat on the beach thinking of our plans when we were thirty and he had just left the army; we had planned to sit together on this beach with a minimal mortgage and commitments in England, a little business in Greece to pay the bills and all by the time we were forty; now I'd be paying a mortgage until I am bloody sixty. I didn't allow myself too much time to dwell on stuff but I couldn't help wondering how different our lives could have been if it weren't for the bloody illness…

Of course they got me off the island without having to restrain me and fight me onto the plane, but it does get harder every time I leave; all three of us have always liked the Greek Islands, the closest peaceful sunny holiday you can get. I got home and back to it and was pleased to see a few weeks down the line from having started his anti-depressants he was looking and sounding much happier than he had for a while. Maybe we could get through this after all.

Still no word from his pension or the hospital so he was still concerned about money and the high levels of medication he was taking, but his mood had lifted, so me and Dave could make him laugh about stuff to keep him going. Laughter really is the best tonic for picking up your spirits and feeding your soul. (I wonder if I got that off a birthday card)

One Saturday morning towards the end of the month I was sat drinking my cuppa when the postman knocked on the door with a big envelope. I thought someone had been ordering stuff off eBay; it turned out to be the pack of "evidence" that had been gathered by the Veterans' agency to turn down his claim for a pension.

I started to read through his information, letters from Nopal to our GP and to the agency, information from the other hospital where he stayed. I couldn't believe some of the stuff I was reading. The hospital notes from our local hospital on the first day he was admitted made extremely interesting reading.

Things like 'he pulled the radiator off the wall', had turned into 'he had pulled the stop valve off the end of it'. They also had written stuff that we had told them on admission down wrong, I also think some of the dates had been changed on information.

Some of Nopal's notes had been included; the "mistake" that had cost Rex his driving licence had just a small amount of space in his notes despite being the single biggest thing since he left hospital that could have caused a relapse; the issues with drink and cannabis are also there and well out of proportion to his true mental health problem, leading me to believe that Nopal was prejudice against my old man, judging him for having problems with binge drinking and the occasional use of cannabis.

Last year when a slight trace of cannabis and no alcohol were involved in his illness, an attack and sunstroke had also been evident but not mentioned to the agency, part of the reason that his pension had been turned down was that they believed that Rex is a hardcore substance abuser. I wonder where they get that idea from? Not only had Nopal written to them, there is evidence that they had spoken to him on the phone in December just before they turned down his claim; I can only imagine what he had told them. He doesn't know the truth so he couldn't tell it because he had refused to listen to what the problem was.

Nopal had also suggested that we go to relate to sort out our marital problems; I wanted to kill him. I am a believer in talking through problems; I do that everyday sorting out problems for 80 clients and nine staff members at work by communicating and focusing on what people need to "function". I am a good people person, I am good at relationships, building them, maintaining and cherishing them, and even with my limited knowledge I know relationships can only be fixed when both cogs are turning, and unfortunately one of our cogs was going too slow, but he thought it would make things better...

Our label was complete... And in reality Nopal had made mistakes all along in diagnosing and treating Rex; made a fatal error that had lost Rex his licence, he had been a consultant psychiatrist in a hospital where they have to use bully-boy tactics and police cells to look after vulnerable people when they are most vulnerable and now it seemed he had a hand in stopping the pension payments.
I wasn't surprised again; Rex getting a bit more money to live on would have meant less stress over the last months and that would have helped his health no end.

The information from his early appointments with Nopal's clinic were not sent in; if you remember back it was one of Nopal's assistants that spoke of PTSD nearly four years ago... They hadn't passed that information on.

Filling in all of the gaps we could clearly see why the claim had been turned down to some extent. It was disappointing that everything took so long with the agency and the service from the NHS. What a surprise both government run services with extremely bad standards, but you can't change things like that, you just keep going to work so that the government can take your tax to provide the crap...

Down the Road

There's a few people I know with quite serious mental health problems; some of them go to work in all different jobs... some live on benefits, some of them use drugs and/or drink and quite a few are addicted to the drugs used to "treat" them by doctors.

Go back to the statistic; one in four people, and count up the people down your street or around your office and think how many people are living with serious illnesses; people like Rex, people for whom the real problem is that they have got the invisible illness, the upstairs problem; the dreaded curse..."Madness".

Maybe it matters to me because I chose to deal with people everyday. At home, the staff I manage and the client group for whom we provide services. I see the misery that the bad treatment of mental health brings for lots of people trying to "cope". Life can get us all down at some stage but you assume that whatever bit of your body breaks down it will be fixed on the NHS...I wanted to tell you all about what you can expect in reality if it happens to you. Of course evidence would suggest that the standard of care available very much depends on the area you live in, postcode Mental Health Treatment...

I was on the last chapter of the book by the end of July then something else outrageous happened as well, as things kicking of at work again. I got a phone call late one night, someone close to my heart and quite probably one of the most seriously mentally ill people I know who has serious drink issues had stabbed her partner...
They thought the partner was dead. My heart started racing as my phone start ringing with people unable to comprehend what had happened.

I'll give you a brief description of this person's illness; it's not very different to thousands of others. By the tender age of sixteen mental health issues had been identified, to be honest and at the risk of upsetting people she had not had the best start, it had been ok in the fact she had been fed and clothed and look after to some extent, but both her parents drank and often in times of stress the drinking would get out of control.

Seeing drink used like that gave her the licence she needed, for the next couple of years she used drink and drugs to mask the problems. Self harming became a way of life; cutting herself served as self punishment for being such a bad person. She is a genuine, lovely person underneath.

She felt she had failed as a person; she hated herself but loved her kids and others in her life, but how you can show anyone else love when you don't like your self very much is beyond me; her illness turned her into an out of control mum.

Things got worse and worse, not enough services were available to help her out, diagnosis and treatment weren't easy for her to get. Untreatable personality disorder was mentioned early on.

The local police were constantly picking her up; even after her lovely little daughter came along, even though good parenting skills were evident and she looked after the baby for about two years, her mental health was not stable enough for her to care for herself let alone anyone else; eventually the babies' dad took over full time care to allow her to get "her head sorted" she hadn't turned twenty yet.

The guy was older and continued to support her and she had more than enough contact with the child, but by now substance abuse was her form of self-medicating; she had started drinking too much again, she was lucky he was such a good man; he cared about her a lot.

A couple of years passed and she had another kid, this time the dad is not so dependable but she tries her very best to cope on her own. She managed to look after the baby, his basic needs but she was still abusing herself with drink and any sharp object...

She was very quickly trapped in a vicious circle, wanting help, needing help. Social Services had got involved and after a while the baby was taken into care. Social services had given some support but they didn't have enough staff or resources to help properly. They quickly told her to stop drinking and got her help; some medication and group therapy if she wanted it; but with no full package of intense care for the mental health problems on offer trying to stop the drinking like this was setting her up to fail; really social services were using her child to try and bribe her to stop drinking for months

.

She did try; she had weeks of sobriety, she took the medication, she wanted to keep her baby but deep inside she knew she'd lose him. Only she will ever know how big the demons are that her drink problem was masking. Eventually that's how the government chose to help her, by taking the only thing away from her that kept her going.

I understand the need for safety for the child, I'm paid to care and know about that sort of thing but they could have done more; at 23 she is not much more than a kid herself.

It was a shame because with no one to look after, nothing to keep her on the straight and narrow we all knew she would fall right of the wagon again... The local authorities were so concerned about her behaviour that they wouldn't let any family members care for the baby; so he went into foster care. She wasn't a real threat to her kids, she just wasn't well enough to look after them. Her unstable mental health often meant she was a danger to herself but not to others, she had only ever self harmed; no one else had been hurt physically.

One night an ambulance had had to come and take her away from her house as she sat on her kitchen floor cutting herself and drinking nail polish remover.

Tan laughed as she told me about this; the first thing she had asked the ambulance driver for was a light, the reason she had got into that state was because she didn't have a light for her fag in a round about way...

I have been honest and told you all along I like people that laugh at extreme times; it breaks the tension and to be honest the biggest mental health problem that kills people is stress…

Laughter eases stress; it's a fact (I think!).

They obviously declined her request due to the combustible nature of her chosen tipple that night. On the many other occasions she had been in hospital and the police cells when she had taken overdoses, various serious cuts and self inflicted wounds of all types. She has drunk herself into comas and near to death on several occasions; she is a seriously ill person patched up in A&E then left without proper care for years.

As well as being bonkers she also happens to be one of the brightest, articulate people I have ever met. She has many good qualities but for most of her short life her problem has driven a wedge between her and her family, causing them and her untold heartbreak.

Just after the baby was taken she met a new man; a drinker, someone to get drunk with. Again this time she had gone for an older man, someone who really seemed to care.

The second baby's dad had been a young lad her own age and with problems of his own…

One issue from her childhood was her relationship with her Dad, so it is text book, the replacement of him that drives her towards these older men.

The relationship was doomed; two people who were totally compatible but with a shared drink problem was always going to be an explosive relationship. From what I understand they got on really well but then they went on benders…

Over the first days when I had got the call my mind was racing, firstly with concern that the guy was ok. He must love her because I knew that she hadn't seen the police or the hospital over the months she had been with him. I knew from my own experiences that if the police had stopped picking her up over the last months it was because he had been trying to look after her; he must be a decent bloke of sorts.

My mind then went straight to the fact that I hoped that they were looking after her properly; as soon as she stops drinking after a bender she starts having fits. She also has the self harm stuff that we all worry about.

Putting the pieces of what happened that day together it seems he has been hurt before trying to stop her from cutting herself, but he stayed with her.
I gather most of these injuries have happened as he has tried to wrestle knives from her to stop the self harm.

Mostly this happens when they had both been drinking; they had been drinking and arguing all day the day this happened. Once again he went to take a knife off of her; she was going to hurt herself and she cut his wrist; it was an accident, she wanted to hurt herself not him; she loved him.

This may sound extreme to some people but thinking about the way that they live it was probably "normal" for them; it was how they had lived for months…
This time it was a bit deeper than before so he staggered off to the hospital and got it stitched up. Not knowing where he had gone and far too ill and drunk to make sense of what had happened, she went to her family.
As her mum and sister started to try and sort out the mess, cleaning her and the mess up, he came back, wanting to look after her again; he was claiming undying love for her. They were dependant on each other; two desperate drunks trying to look after each other. Her mum and sister asked him to leave, but he wanted to stay.
This bit is pure speculation by me but the way her mind works I think by this stage she had blamed him for it all; he had gone to the hospital and she couldn't remember where he had gone; in her head in her current situation it would have all been his fault.
Forgetting the reality of the situation was better than admitting that she had hurt one of the few people she had left in the world. Despite her Mum and Sister trying to calm her down she had wound herself up

to the max having little or no control over her mind or thoughts by that stage, she lost the plot and stabbed him again…

It all happened quickly; she just flipped. In reality what had happened had been a tragic accident, caused largely by the fact that a man with serious drink issues had been left trying his very best to look after a person with serious mental health problems and a drink problem too. She was bonkers and he chose to be there with her, she only ever hurt herself in the past and he had bravely or stupidly got in the way of that.
The situation then quickly turned into a tragic event in which she had committed a terrible crime.

She was kept in a police cell for days whilst they gathered evidence and took statements, her boyfriend refused to press charges; he knew what had happened so the police had to make a case; they were digging up dirt…

She's now on remand; locked up for hurting her bloke, a guy who knows she is too ill too be in prison; someone else that has desperately needed help has now had her life ruined by her illness.

This is only a few miles down the road from us; her ongoing health problems and subsequent detention are the work of the same Primary Care Trust and Police Force as the ones that dealt with Rex.
My man had been locked in a cell for nearly 2 days and sectioned twice for breaking a radiator, then again for slashing my sofa…

She had hurt herself and ended up in A&E; kicking off on several occasions and had serious issues for six years, but she has had to wait till she has hurt someone else before they locked her up. They obviously never cared about her enough to section her for being a danger to herself or others as described in the Mental Health Act. You know the law used to protect vulnerable people when they are "ill"?
Only when her "mad, bizarre, dangerous self-harming" behaviour had affected someone else had they got involved; once to take her kid off

her and now to lock her up. In a prison how can that be fair? Schools and the NHS; the only two big things our government have been left to "manage" and look at the state of them; their failure has quickly filled our prisons.

People don't matter as much as striving to achieve goals, standards and targets. Political campaigns are run on words like 'aims' and 'objectives'; no one promises us anything anymore. It's a way of ensuring we aren't all disappointed all the time. More money is spent on administration of the health service than would ever be spent on delivering services.

All those times she had come to the health authority's attention for self harm; she'd been allowed to go home to do it again and again and again. In some strange ways her being locked up has been a relief for her family; someone other than them is now watching her twenty-four hours a day, something she has needed for a long time.
There's not one of them that wouldn't give their right arm for her to get the right help she needs in a hospital with specialised mental health therapy to give her the life back she deserves so much...
But she ends up in prison; intense people management at its worse.

Our prison population has been pushed to the limits with people like her being locked up instead of looked after... Detention under the mental health act is for people who are a danger to themselves or others. How much violent crime is committed by people like her who need locking up when they are harming themselves to stop them harming others?

We all know the way the hospitals are managed; under staffed, never enough beds, but in mental health they get away with it again and again; locking people in prisons, police cells and expensive private hospitals.

Ignoring the epidemic that is sweeping through our country...

Our local hospitals mental health care ratings have consistently dropped over the last years. Don't get me wrong I think the overall performance has been improving; we have got some new units for other illness to push the overall performance of the hospital up, making money on renal procedures and heart scans… things they can profit on... That's the only way to plug the millions of pounds deficits they have had in the last years.

You need people, not drugs or fancy machinery to fix people with Mental Health Problems; the NHS have made it clear they don't want to invest in people, spending a lot on machinery makes more profit. Most of our own newly qualified nurses leave to go work in countries where they are valued, and that leaves hospitals relying on relief staff and agency workers. A few hardcore, tougher-than-nails nurses can usually be found in most wards; these people are the backbone of the whole system and they are fighting what appears to be a losing battle; my heart goes out to them.

Often the government are behind campaigns; blaming drink and drugs for causing the massive rise in people becoming mentally unwell. In this country self inflicted "illnesses" can't be the governments fault; that way they get away with not treating the problems that we know often lie under those addictions.

Rex was neither a danger to himself or others with the right care; if you remember, he had been "ill" for nearly two weeks before he went in hospital, a week in Greece with Fred John Wayne and the others; the flight back (bless easy jet and all that lot), the two days at home… No previous aggressive history known to the police or the health authority and they manage to get him taken to a police cell and sectioned for hurting a radiator belonging to the hospital and shouting; after less than three hours in the care of the local hospital. She nearly kills herself several times and they let her get on with it for five years…

They, in this instance are our Local Authority; they provide our health service on behalf of the government. Thanks for nothing on her behalf.

My heart breaks for her situation; I just can't believe this is a productive, fair or humane way for a local health service to look after sick people at all. Consistent seems to point to consistently bad, across our county anyway, they don't seem to care about mental well being.

She could get a life sentence.

Nearly There

I really don't know how but the end of the book has caught up with real life; it's August, it's raining and life goes on. I am not sure in what direction it's going in, but things can only get better I always think.

Eventually, a couple of weeks ago he got to meet his new consultant. Again I had to go with him; he won't meet new doctors by himself. He just manages speaking to the GP he has had for the last seven years. I rushed back from work and we went to the appointment. To put Rex at ease the doctor started the session by telling us that he didn't have an appointment to see Rex, but he could spare a few minutes. He told us he hadn't read any notes and that he knew nothing; he asked "what was the problem?" like he'd just asked for the time off a stranger in the street. What was the problem?
He was lucky I didn't jump up and smack him on the nose. I remained in my seat by thinking about my job; knowing the way they dealt with any shouting in this hospital; I didn't want carting off and sectioning for voicing my concern…

I couldn't believe it, Rex sat wide eyed wondering what he could say in a few minutes… to tell the doctor what the problem is, was, or has been. Where do you start?

After a few minutes of silence and stammering I took over. Something that I have been trying hard not to do in the last months, but after the farce of him being "looked after" by Nopal it was time someone took his problems seriously. In the last weeks he had started to get better, his mood had been lifted, he had even been cracking jokes and making us laugh. Amazingly he had even spoken to a couple of his old mates in the last weeks. His ability to cope had vastly been improved; only a few small panic attacks…
No miracle involved; most of this was down to the anti-depressants that I had demanded from the GP, but who cares why it was getting better? It was just good that it was. Knowing Rex like I do, I knew this meeting with the doc would freak him out; it had started with the

doctor putting him on edge, Rex would have to work hard to get over it…

I told the Doctor what had been happening; by now I had shrunk it down; I could now manage it in about seven and a half minutes. Why has this bloody book taken months I ask myself again?

The appointment ended quickly with one of Rex's medications being reduced by half. A sign that the doctor believed he was over-medicated maybe? It was a quick decision for someone who'd known him ten minutes and had, by his own admission, no idea of what had been happening.

I didn't want to moan; I knew the signs to watch for if there was going to be any ill affects of such a rapid reduction. Once again, my years of experience and training were going to come in handy.

Dave managed to get a job; at last he is a conscientious team member in one of our large, local stores; selling household items, lighting and rugs. Over night his confidence had grown and he has also managed to score a ticket to our local music festival. We have laughed as he prepares for it, remembering the major panic attack last year when it didn't arrive; over looked in the madness of Rex's breakdown…
He had only been out of hospital for a few weeks when that had happened. How that could be a year ago I am not sure; it caused loads of stress and panic, but here we were a year later laughing about it.

I have always been proud of Dave; he is an amazing person. Already at eighteen he has learnt more lessons about life than some people learn in a long lifetime. I am afraid to say as his mother he has had it hard; sometimes living with illness brings stress for the whole family.

Dave is always quick to point out that it's been easier for him than for lots of others, and without giving anything away his generation seem a lot more open than ours about madness; it's helped him knowing that this is not only happening to us; other members of his crew have their own issues within their own families; but the kids seem to be able to talk about it to each other and accept it as "normal".

Not having a proper "normal" anymore has made life a lot easier in a lot of ways.

It makes my heart glad that maybe the next generation might grow up without baggage like us oldies; that still worry about being classed as mad.

Dave has a strong sense of family values, and right and wrong he cares about others; for the most part so does his mates. He is very close to his cousins and always has someone to turn to; he gets by.

Dave often congratulates me on keeping it together; he knows when I am at the end of my "tether". I do have quite a stressful life, more than some, less than others; to be honest sometimes it has been a hundred times harder to keep going than it would be to give up, sell the house and spend the money on crack! Joking, but you know what I mean. Shirley Valentine sounds like a good choice of film for the mood today...

Dave often laughs at me when I get in a "strop"; the same as most teenagers these days he has a self-contained, smelly pit in the centre of the house, commonly called a bedroom. A space packed to the rafters with computers, music making equipment, guitars, a double bed; facility to lay and watch a dvd with no more strain than moving a finger.
Often decorated with various plates, cups, banana skins, food wrappers, half eaten food items and, on occasions with other six foot lanky little men. He has a sanctuary away from his mad mother and father...

In the last year I have had two occasions when he has had to look after me, making me tea and telling me jokes. I have had what I would term "proper depression"; no daylight, no phone, loads of crying and a bit of self pity. Both times I managed to shake it off within two days; it's not ideal having your kid look after you, but he has learnt a very valuable lesson; to keep going. Get up every day and get on with your life; whether it's good or bad. Life isn't a rehearsal, so you have to get up and get on with it, and enjoy it as much as you can.

I have a friend, Carol, who suffers from Bi Polar disorder or "manic depression" as it's commonly called. We have spent ages talking about it. When we have spoken she has often asked how I manage to stop the depression from carrying on for days. Years ago an old psychiatrist told me about coping, by visualising depression has a dark cloud coming over my world. It was just after my dad had died; I must have been talking about that. Since then I have worked hard to blow it away whilst the cloud is still forming; recognising the "symptoms" early to stop it making my "world" dark, it has worked for me for the last few years.

Carol has also tried it and had some success, you have to ride the mania; clean you house, dance, knit a jumper, make it work for you.

I haven't said one bad thing about Dave in this book, and to be honest there is not a lot of bad stuff to say; he is fantastic, I often wonder where he came from but then I stop and give us the credit. Despite everything else in our lives we have managed to keep our heads above water and produce him; we must have done something right.

Whilst I do feel a little guilty for what he has been through, in other ways I know that he has had a better start than we had; more support, more love and many more choices. He has controlled himself for the last four or so years; I have just advised on consequences. This has allowed him freedom to develop himself as a person; he's done a good job too. Allowing him this freedom has prevented a lot of teen arguments, making our home life more peaceful than most. In many ways Rex has been difficult to live with; Dave has been easy. He'd be great on Big Bro, he'd be the best contestant ever; he is a good housemate.

So when I say the poor kid, I don't want anyone feeling sorry for him or us, because we all know our little family will survive.

Not too many things about our government wind me up; why let it? Everything is spin for the media these days. Meanwhile the fundamental failures of the services they "provide" are causing problems for us all; I am going to have my last moan; this could be my only book!

The fact that repossession of people's homes is on the rise joins my list, due to the fact that we could easily have fallen into the "spending" trap that's causing it.

Many of us have made money up to some point on property in the last years. Some people are spending their equity; that's their business I say, yet it seems the government don't like us enjoying our own money; so to stop spending they put up interest rates most of our biggest outgoings are determined by interest rates.

The banks aren't prepared to lose their "assets", our homes so they put interest rates up, monthly payments go the same way, causing stress for most of us. Mortgage payments come first for most people, but the lack of disposable income in homes for many reasons not all "self inflicted" spending on credits cards although that is playing a big part too but in the end you find you can't pay the mortgage. You lose your home first.

Why don't they just regulate "irresponsible" lending; instead of having thousands of people at threat of losing their family homes; their place of safety. Can you imagine being unable to provide a bed for your kid to sleep in tonight

Working with homeless people makes you consider everyone, not only the people obviously homeless and on the street. The only reason I can see this being allowed to happen by the government is because it makes them money too…

Irresponsible lending is on the rise, I worked with a woman a few years ago who had 23 grand of debt, she had claimed benefits for ten years but had still been able to apply for credit to that level, with the help of the CAB we declared her bankrupt not the best option but these lenders need to learn. In the service I run, we support 60 people mostly on benefits and 95% of them have debt problems.

There but for the "grace of god"; maybe if things had gone differently when Rex left the Army we could have lost our home when he became too ill to work. Lots of people do.

People only sign agreements to give up the rights to their home when they are desperate and vulnerable.

So many things in this country controlled by the government make us vulnerable as citizens; losing your home is the biggest worry in someone's life, so rising bank charges to "slow down spending" makes us all vulnerable to some degree (unless you are well off enough to not know how much your mortgage payment is or when it's due). No offence meant but my guess is money isn't causing the real problems, if you are fortunate enough to be in that position.

The failing NHS is still crap in many ways; we might have more doctors but that just means less money available for treatments needed; so arguments like ours over the little things like the right medication to keep you alive when you have cancer, or appropriate treatments when you are mad have clearly been sacrificed at patient level to fill targets like having more doctors.

I wasn't so outraged years ago when we saw the first load of "postcode" health care, the first thing that went into the "lottery" was fertility treatment. If I am honest at the time I can remember thinking it wasn't life threatening; my heart did twitch for the couples but not to any great affect.

The NHS should be about the right treatment for those people that need it, when they need it, regardless of what the "government" are saying is the priority at the moment.

If you have paid for the health service surely you should be entitled to the service you need when you need it? That's why we pay for a health service isn't it? Private health care would probably be cheaper but we don't have the choice do we?

A couple could work for their whole lives contributing to this country; may never need anything more from the health care system than fertility treatment and the usual check ups for the rest of their lives. They could be denied all they need when they need it.

I saw a lottery winner being interviewed the other week; he had worked his whole life, had a windfall in his retirement and ended up buying himself a new knee as a priority... What a smack in the gob to contribute all those years; and all you need is a knee to enjoy your retirement. I bet the actual cost of the replacement part is minimal.

Over the years many services have gone the same way;
Mental Health Services I have to mention because that's what has failed for Rex but I am sure there are others.

How can what happened to him be called "care"?

The slow improvement in education means still too many school leavers are being left out when it comes to being supported at the critical time when they are most vulnerable; "the teenage years".

As far as I am concerned those years don't finish till a kid turns twenty, but our government are still failing them from finishing school, sixteen, and seventeen with nothing to do. Not everyone wants to go to college and in a lot of areas real apprenticeships are few and far between.

In "my day" you would be straight on Youth Training Schemes; mine was in a Newsagent's. Before I was put on that me and my friend Debbie went to claim dole; we thought it would be novel, not many people on the dole in those days...There were jobs; we just couldn't be arsed. We were sixteen; the world owed us a living, no rich folks so the dole was the easy option.

I was sixteen I claimed the money; "twenty eight quid" a fortnight for six weeks before they found me my "job".

It paid me twenty five quid a week; earning just a little more than you get on benefits. It was all about being taught skills instead of sitting on your arse, all it taught me was how to bloody get up early as the people who owned the shop, lovely as they were, got me to open up most mornings to give them a lie in. In "those" days only the newsagent would be open before nine in the morning, maybe the odd garage but nowhere else.

It was bloody hard work for little money.

Today at sixteen they become job seekers...

From what I am seeing some of them might look forever; it took Dave months to find a job and some of his mates are still trying. Within weeks of my government training starting I had got off my butt and got a "proper job"; I knew I would always have to provide for myself so the most money for the least hours became my priority for a while.

The other big issue I think is the reality of appropriate support for people with substance abuse issues; like the young lady down the road from me. Poor mental health triggers these addictions, then they get in the way of asking for or getting treatment; more people are taking the blame for their own problems as local authorities offer medication to "Detox" in the community.

Little or no support, but at least they can record it as an attempt to "help folks". How can people do it without the support of the right services? They say they are helping but things aren't getting better; it all contributes to "us" taking the blame for their shortfalls in my opinion.

All of these things are making more people fall into that "class" of vulnerable; that's why I didn't think we had a story to tell. To be honest the issues that come from the things the government are getting wrong have become a way of life; not many families today can say that they don't have some sort of issue related to these things, just like us; money worries, poor mental or physical health, wayward teenagers, substance abuse, unemployment...

To put down on paper what has happened to us and how we have managed to cope has been strange. I still don't know what it is myself; I just keep the belief that bad times always pass; that keeps me going, happy seconds, happy minutes, happy hours, happy days and so on....

Don't worry if you will be happy tomorrow make yourself happy today.

What I wanted to do most of all was tell the story of how some soldiers are left struggling to cope with life after the forces; some are war veterans like my husband. Experiences in the forces may be different but the one thing they all have in common is to make good soldiers the army bends your mind, putting you into abnormal situations constantly that has to have long term affects on your mental health.

Joining the forces is a choice that is clear; no one is forced by anything other than limited options for teenagers in our society.

Leaving your wife and baby to go to war at twenty one is not a normal day at work; seeing war first hand must be traumatic.
Getting some sort of Post Traumatic Syndrome after leaving the military environment depends on many factors, your ability to cope as a person, your sense of identity, and your emotional stability.
Environmental factors like family community, employment housing and support are obviously very important too.

Rex has told me he feels lucky to have had my support over the years; I have helped him control his illness for long enough. We met quite a few people in the weeks he was locked up that spoke to us both about the fact that he wasn't the first "soldier" they had looked after recently with the same story.

My colleagues and I also come across a fair few vets working in supported housing; soldiers who have been unsupported, dealing with the same issues as Rex; but these have often crossed the line from substance use to substance abuse and ended up offending, and I for one know they will never get the help they need and deserve under the current system.
Firing on all cylinders there are few forces bigger than me and I haven't been able to get the right help for Rex, so without some changes to the "system" things will only get worse for these vets; often they don't think that they deserve help trained to be proud asking for it is hard and when it isn't easily available they can't or won't keep asking.
Currently no full set of figures exists to back up which environment combination is the worst for veterans, but I am sure we can all guess

the worst your situation the worse the symptoms of your illness would be…The way this illness develops; it makes pushing people away the only option, it's that or admit how bad it actually is.

I will be having a site on the "tinternet" web thing going under the same name as the book and I hope to set up a group to start measuring some of this stuff; I keep telling everyone the only way to get through the day is to worry about "facts"; establish the facts and work on those.
Feel free to join the group…

Early diagnosis and treatment of the illness is the only thing that could make a difference; support at the start. Freedom from institutes isn't always what it seems to be; missing it is inevitable, coping with missing it is a different ball game.

One of the main causes of re-offending according to many prolific offenders is that they are at least "looked after", and have structure in prison. You can't often get back in the army even if you want to.
Getting the right treatment early on is never going to happen; treating anything in its early stages gets the best results, but soldiers are taught to get on with it, and when you can't deal with stuff go for a drink... So that's what they do when they leave the army, and for a lot of people that means a quick decent into alcohol use and abuse just like Rex. Thankfully Rex had a safety net.

I will, I am sure, spend a fair few months if not years supporting Rex; to give him chance to get on with his life. He was given a poem by Gordon at the first hospital and I am not sure where it is from but I will share it with you.

Soldiers should never be forgotten yet even in this day and age they still are; they join up to protect our country, they don't pick the fights they just fight them it's a disgrace.
Don't Worry

When you are a soldier you can be in one of two places;
A dangerous place or a safe place
If you are in a safe place don't worry

If you are in a dangerous place you can be one of two things;
One is wounded and the other is not
If you're not wounded don't worry

If you are wounded it can be dangerous or slight;
If it's slight don't worry
If it's dangerous one of two things will happen;

You'll die or you'll recover
If you recover don't worry
If you die you can't worry

In these circumstances a soldier never worries.

He believed in that for weeks; no worry, no stress, just chilling out, getting better; every soldier needs a safe place. Every person needs a safe place. I want Rex to join some campaigns; everyone needs to fight for something my next book might be a campaign for cheaper fair trade chocolate.

A few weeks ago his new consultant told him he does have complex post traumatic stress; so he is now a little relieved. Even up to this point he still thought that doctors didn't believe he was ill. He only believed it truly for the three weeks he was in Waterloo last year when they took time to talk to him about all of his symptoms.

Nopal had told him there was nothing wrong except the pot smoking in the past, and last year when the doctors were saying it he was too ill or too medicated to take it on board after he had been in Swan.

The doctor now looking after him has made the right diagnosis and told Rex direct; Rex feels like there has been a breakthrough, there has in Rex's mind anyway. I hope things can move forward for him now they have the right diagnosis locally.

Small victories remember; if you're safe and you have something to fight for you have a reason to get up and get on.

Time is ticking by and now Halloween, Bonfire Night, and Chrimble are all back upon us, so I have to draw it to an end. Ghost hunting to be done, Fireworks to watch, mulled wine to drink and of course shopping to do; sure signs it is bloody winter again; crap weather and good festivals.

I hate winter but this year at least I will be warm; the first year in five that I will have a working fire in my house during the winter months. Like I said before getting workmen in has always been traumatic, I have had them in this year, I put my foot down; it's my house.

Eco logs here we come; a nice real fire for comfort, warmth and general well-being…

Whoops I got so involved in finishing this in the last months that I nearly forgot the other major thing I need to do this year. I have to find a new job; "my deal" runs out at Christmas. My job no longer "viable"; that was another driver in writing the book, the bank may soon be coming for my house. See, drama again. I do need to find a new job but I know something will come up, it usually does, I am not worried.

In all honesty I would like to start my own charity to help out people like us; soldiers and their families suffering from the effects of this illness

We'll see in the future but for now it's been work, write, sleep, work, write, sleep. When I don't have the writing, I'll take up knitting or something; scarves and socks for Christmas, keeping people warm would be good for the environment and my budget!

I really can't see work changing much in the next few months I'll get on with it 110 % until I find something new. Like I said before things there are getting better in our little team, adjusting to change is hard for everyone; the last eighteen months have been "bonkers". Change at work then crisis at home in the blink of an eye; all those months have flown by. When starting my new job, two years had seemed an age away.

The poor sods have just got used to me and now I have to move on but this time they won't have too much to change; they'll just have to get used to someone new, someone probably less demanding than me.

I give a lot so I expect a lot; that's who I am, take me or leave me is a question of choice…

Most people I come across take me I work hard I am honest and straight forward. It's been an eventful five years and I have met many fantastic people in my job I will miss them but I will get to keep some as friends. I knew it was only for two years, I am just shocked how quickly it's gone.

So I best get this book finished so you all can read it and let me know what you think. Could I give up my day job and lay on a bed writing stories and eating chocolate? My third title could be "the woman that exploded"

I asked the men in my house what they thought about the ending, bearing in mind neither of them have read much, as I have written it. Rex and Dave came up with the following; they know the story, they have lived it too, this is just my take on it remember. I have tried to be fair.

Rex said if he was the main character in a tragic tale he felt he should be killed off at the end; all three of us are prone to being dramatic! Acting must be in our genes.

Dave's response on how he would create this dramatic end to his father's tragedy, beloved papa would be covered in "paper cuts", and then put in vodka to pickle him… We still don't take life too seriously, as you can tell.

This book is not a tragic tale, neither is it an option to kill him in such a way; enough vodka to cover him would cost far too much, not counting the fact that it could get a lot of people in the mood for a party; a waste of perfectly good vodka!

Our health service could have caused a tragedy but we managed to change our fate by fighting the system. It wasn't easy

What choice do we have but to soldier on together until he's well enough to look after himself again? His illness only truly affects him now he manages to control the symptoms that have affected us badly in the past.

There is light at the end of the tunnel and the nightmare is ending we might even win his pension claim he could buy some more private treatment.

His new "understanding" consultant on the NHS suggested that's what he should do if he felt he needed therapy Rex should get me to get more funding for it; that was at his last appointment a few weeks ago our lives have moved on but they still can't provide treatment for him to help him move on. He can't stay at home forever, he's only 38. He needs support and therapy to get over this illness, a bit like physiotherapy for your broken bone.

We are left wondering why he can't get help for his illness for free on the NHS as I end the book; the same question as when I started could still drive me mad if I let it.

However we are loads happier and much stronger so they (our local Primary Care Trust) can get stuffed we will sort it out ourselves again.

We will get him more treatment privately and one day they will apologise for the way they have "treated" him. The label they obviously attached to him as a "dangerous madman" last year will be challenged they got it wrong I will make sure they admit it.

Not just for Rex but for the thousands of other Veterans who don't get what they deserve: they need looking after and from what I can see they are being locked up, two very different things I think.

If Dave starts amassing Vodka and Paper I won't leave him alone with his Dad.